Guide
To
Higher Grade
Chemistry

by

Iain Brand

Principal Teacher of Chemistry
St Margaret's High School, Airdrie

ISBN 0 7169 3230 x

© Iain Brand, 1999.

ROBERT GIBSON . Publisher
17 Fitzroy Place, Glasgow, G3 7SF

TO THE STUDENT

This *Guide to Higher Grade Chemistry* has been written for students who are preparing for the Scottish Qualifications Authorities Higher Grade award in Chemistry.

The Higher Grade Chemistry course is split into three units . . .

> Unit 1 — **"Energy Matters"**
> Unit 2 — **"The World of Carbon"**
> Unit 3 — **"Chemical Reactions"**

To gain a course award you need to pass the internal assessments of each unit, as well as the external SQA examination.

This book has been specifically designed to help you **study** and **revise** for **tests** and **examinations**. The work of each unit is split up into sections, which include . . .

> lists **of learning outcomes**,
> **word lists** of important chemical terms,
> a concise coverage of the **knowledge and understanding**,
> details of **prescribed practical activities** (PPAs),
> and a **"glossary"** of chemistry terms used in the Higher units.

Each of these sections can be used to support your study for **Higher Grade Chemistry**. Remember, organised revision, using a variety of approaches, is the basis for success in all tests and examinations . . . **Good luck !**

Iain Brand
1999

CONTENTS

UNIT 1
ENERGY MATTERS

REACTION RATES

Chemistry is all about **chemical reactions** and the formation of **new substances**. Chemical reactions happen all around us, in nature, in the home and in industry. This section introduces theories on how reactions occur, and the factors which affect their speed, so that we can understand and control the course of chemical reactions. ✦

At the end of this section you should be able to . . . ✔

Describe how a chemical reaction occurs by using the *collision theory*. ❐
Explain the terms *activation energy*, *activated complex* and *collision geometry*. ❐
Describe how to follow the rate of a reaction by measuring changes in concentration, mass or volume of the reactants or products. ❐
Give examples of the units used for measuring reaction rates. ❐
Calculate the average rate of a reaction from a graph or given data. ❐

Explain the link between rate and the reciprocal of the time taken, $\frac{1}{T}$. ❐

Describe how to investigate the effect of concentration on reaction rate (*ppa*) ❐
Explain why changes in concentration affect the rate of a reaction. ❐
Describe how to investigate the effect of particle size on reaction rate. ❐
Explain why changes in particle size affect the rate of a reaction. ❐
Describe how to investigate the effect of temperature on reaction rate (*ppa*). ❐
Explain the link between temperature and kinetic energy of particles. ❐
Explain the effect of temperature on the rate of a reaction by using kinetic energy distribution diagrams, etc. ❐
Describe a *photochemical reaction* and explain how it works. ❐
Define, with examples, *heterogeneous* and *homogeneous catalysts*. ❐
Explain, with examples, the action of a *surface catalyst* and what is meant by *catalyst poisoning*. ❐
Name some industrial catalysts and explain why they may need to be regenerated or replaced after some time. ❐
Explain how catalytic convertors work and can be poisoned. ❐
Describe the action of an *enzyme*, and give an example in nature. ❐
Describe some uses of enzymes in industry. ❐

WORD LIST

The following words are introduced or used in this topic. You should be able to define, use and give examples of them where appropriate.

activated complex	catalyst poisoning	homogeneous catalyst
activation energy	catalytic cracking	kinetic energy
active sites	collision geometry	photochemical reactions
adsorbed	collision theory	surface catalyst
catalyst	heterogeneous catalyst	temperature

If you are not familiar with the meaning of any of these words, you should refer to the Glossary, where these words are defined.

The speed or **rate** of a chemical reaction can vary greatly, from the very slow to the almost instantaneous . . .

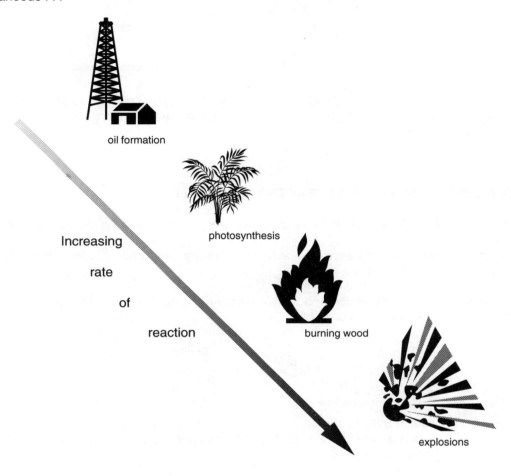

oil formation

photosynthesis

Increasing

rate

of

reaction

burning wood

explosions

COLLISION THEORY

A chemical reaction will only occur when the reacting molecules collide with enough **kinetic energy** or **speed**.
The energy is needed to overcome repulsive forces between atoms and molecules and to start the breaking of bonds.
The minimum kinetic energy needed for a reaction to occur is called the **activation energy (Ea)**.

It is thought that this activation energy is stored, temporarily, in an unstable intermediate called an **"activated complex"**, which breaks down to form the products of the reaction.

Consider the reaction of hydrogen and bromine . . .

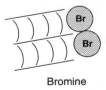

Bromine

Hydrogen

As the reacting molecules collide, their energy is used to overcome repulsive forces and start breaking the bonds between the atoms.

A high energy unstable arrangement of atoms is
formed called the **"activated complex"**.

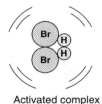

Activated complex

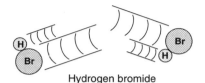

Hydrogen bromide

Energy is given out as new bonds are formed and
the atoms are rearranged into the product
molecule.

COLLISION GEOMETRY AND THE ACTIVATED COMPLEX

In some cases collisions may fail to result in a reaction, even though the molecules have enough
energy.
It is thought that, in these cases, the collision geometry has to be right so that the **activated
complex** can be formed, e.g.

In the reaction of hydrogen and bromine, shown above, the molecules had to collide "side
on" to form the activated complex.

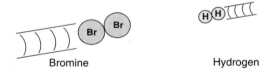

Bromine   Hydrogen

If the molecules collided end on . . .
. . . no reaction occurs as the activated complex cannot be formed if only two of the atoms
come in contact with each other.

MEASURING RATES OF REACTIONS

The rate of a reaction is usually measured by the **change in concentration** of one of the
reactants or products with **time**.

Possible units are . . . **moles per litre per second (mol l^{-1} s^{-1})**.

The **average rate** of a reaction can be calculated if we know the change in concentration of one
of the reactants or products in a given time interval.

$$\text{average rate} = \frac{\text{change in concentration}}{\text{time taken}}$$

Example. In the reaction of sodium thiosulphate with hydrochloric acid the initial concentration of
the acid is 0.5 mol l^{-1}. If this falls to 0.2 mol l^{-1} after 2 minutes what is the average rate
of this reaction?

$$\text{Average rate} = \frac{0 \cdot 5 - 0 \cdot 2}{2 \times 60}$$

$$= \frac{0 \cdot 3}{120}$$

$$= \textbf{0·0025 mol } l^{-1}\textbf{ s}^{-1}$$

INVESTIGATING REACTION RATES

The rate of a reaction can be changed by certain factors such as . . .

concentration — temperature — particle size — catalysts.

In experiments on reaction rate it is not always possible to measure changes in concentration directly. In these cases the rate is often followed by measuring other related changes, for example, mass lost or volume of gas produced, when these are proportional to the change in concentration.

1. Investigating Rate and Concentration

Aim

To investigate the effect of changing concentration on the rate of the reaction between hydrogen peroxide and acidified potassium iodide.

Method

Different concentrations of iodide ions are added to hydrogen peroxide solution.
The reaction is followed by including a small amount of starch and sodium thiosulphate solution in the mixture.
The iodine produced reacts with the thiosulphate and only when this has been used up will the excess iodine turn the mixture black.
This is called a "clock reaction" as we are timing it to the point where the same amount of product has been formed.

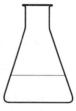

Results

The rate of a "clock reaction" is proportional to $\frac{1}{T}$ as the longer the time, T, the slower the reaction rate.

Therefore, the graph of $\frac{1}{T}$ against concentration, would show how the rate of the reaction was affected by changes in concentration.

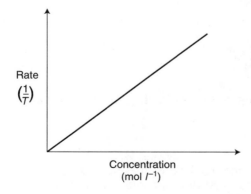

Rate
$(\frac{1}{T})$

Concentration
(mol l^{-1})

As the concentration increases the rate increases proportionally, i.e.,
    double the concentration and you double the rate.

Conclusions

For many reactions the rate is directly proportional to the concentrations of the reactants. The faster reaction rate is due to the increased number of collisions which must occur with higher concentrations of reactants.

2.   Investigating Rate and Particle Size

The reaction of calcium carbonate (marble) with hydrochloric acid produces carbon dioxide gas.

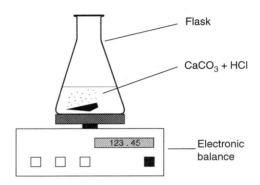

Method

Add excess calcium carbonate to some hydrochloric acid. Measure the loss in mass with time.
Repeat the same experiment with different size pieces of marble chips to investigate the effect of particle size.

Results

A graph of mass lost against time can be used to compare the relative rates of the two experiments. The steeper the slope or gradient of the line the faster the rate of the reaction as this represents a quicker loss in mass.

Note

1.   The rate, and so the gradient of both graphs decrease with time as the concentration of the acid decreases.
2.   The two graphs show the same loss in mass at the end, as the same amount of acid is used in each case and so the same amount of carbon dioxide is released.
3.   The graph show that the smaller chips react faster as their line is steeper at the start of the reaction.

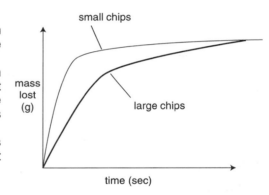

Conclusions

The smaller the particle size the faster the reaction as the total surface area is larger and more collisions will occur.

3.   Investigating Rate and Temperature

Aim

To investigate the effect of changing temperature on the rate of the reaction between oxalic acid and acidified potassium permanganate.

Method

Measured amounts of oxalic acid and permanganate solutions are added together. Initially the mixture is purple due to the permanganate ions, but this colour slowly fades as the reaction takes place. The reaction is timed until the point where the colour completely disappears.
The experiment is then repeated at different temperatures, while keeping the concentrations and total volume of solution constant.

Results

This is another example of a "clock reaction" so the rate will again be proportional to $\frac{1}{T}$.
Therefore a graph of $\frac{1}{T}$ against temperature would show how the rate of the reaction was
affected by temperature.

As the temperature increases there is a
marked increase in rate.

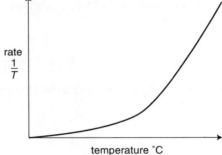

This is a typical Rate/Temperature graph for many chemical reactions.

Conclusions

A small rise in temperature can lead to a large increase in reaction rate. This is due to two
factors, firstly at the higher temperatures more collisions occur as the molecules move
about more quickly and secondly more molecules will have the activation energy needed to
react when they collide.

MORE ABOUT THE TEMPERATURE EFFECT

Temperature is a measure of the average **kinetic energy** or speed of the particles of a
substance.

At any particular temperature the particles of a substance will have a range of kinetic energies
and this can be shown on a **kinetic energy distribution graph**.
The graph below shows the kinetic energy distribution of the particles of a reactant at two
different temperatures. The activation energy for the chemical reaction is also marked on the
graph.

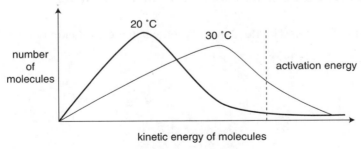

This graph clearly shows that at the higher temperature many more molecules have energies
greater than the activation energy (Ea) and will be able to react when they collide.

PHOTOCHEMICAL REACTIONS

Photochemical Reactions are speeded up by the presence of light.
In these reactions the light energy helps to supply the **activation energy**.

For example the reaction between bromine water and alkanes is faster in sunlight than in the dark.

$$CH_4 + Br_2 \rightarrow CH_3Br + HBr$$

In this example the light energy is used to break the Br — Br bond which initiates the reaction.

CATALYST AND REACTION RATE

A catalyst is a substance which changes the speed of a chemical reaction without being permanently changed itself.
It is thought that catalysts speed up chemical reactions by providing an alternative **reaction pathway** which has a **lower activation energy**.
There are two main types of catalyst.

Homogeneous catalysts are in the **same state as the reactants,**

e.g. Cobalt chloride solution speeds up the formation of oxygen between sodium tartrate solution and hydrogen peroxide solution.
As the reaction proceeds the colour changes from pink to green and back to pink when completed.

This type of catalyst probably works by forming a different activated complex which breaks down to form the same products but requires less energy in its formation

Heterogeneous catalysts are in a **different state from the reactants,**

e.g. solid platinum metal is used in the Ostwald process in the oxidation of ammonia gas to form oxides of nitrogen.

This type of catalyst, called a **surface catalyst**, works by **adsorbing** the reacting molecules on to **active sites** and holding them with weak bonds on its surface.

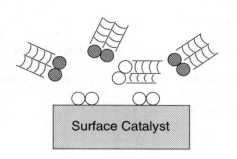

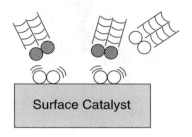

This not only causes the bonds within the molecule to weaken but it also helps the collision geometry.
The reaction occurs on the surface with less energy needed to form the activated complex.

The products are formed and leave the catalyst surface free for further reactions.

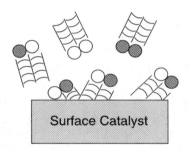

CATALYSTS IN INDUSTRY

Catalysts speed up the formation of products, allowing chemical reactions to occur at lower temperatures.
Catalysts are therefore used in industry to make processes more economic.

There are many examples of industrial catalysts . . .

Iron — in the manufacture of ammonia by the **Haber Process**.
Platinum — in the **catalytic converters** in car exhausts, which change harmful gases into harmless products.
Nickel — to make **margarine** by the hardening vegetable oils.
Platinum — in the manufacture of nitric acid by the **Ostwald Process**.

Many of the catalysts used, like platinum and palladium, are very expensive, but they are cost effective as they do not corrode as easily as the cheaper alternatives, so remain in use for a long time.

CATALYST POISONING

Industrial catalysts can become ineffective after being in use for some time.

Surface catalyst can be **poisoned** when another substance attaches itself to its "active sites" so that less reactant molecules can become adsorbed. If this happens the catalyst has to be **replaced** or **regenerated**, e.g.

Lead and its compounds are **poisons** of transition metal catalysts.
This explains why **leaded** petrol cannot be used in cars with **catalytic converters** as they contain platinum and palladium catalysts.

Catalysts can also be made ineffective by **side-reactions**.
For example, the iron catalyst used in the Haber Process rusts, due to the presence of air and water, and needs to be **replaced** in time.

ENZYMES AND REACTION RATE

Enzymes catalyse the chemical reactions which take place in **living cells**.

Enzymes are complicated protein molecules which usually only speed up one particular reaction and work best under strict conditions of temperature and pH,

   e.g.   *Amylase* — breaks down starch during digestion.

There are also many examples of enzymes which are used in industry . . .

   e.g.   *Invertase* — breaks down sucrose to glucose and fructose.
           Zymase — converts glucose into alcohol in the brewing industry.

How enzymes work is dealt with in more detail in Unit 2, **"Natural Products"**.

ENERGY CHANGES IN CHEMICAL REACTIONS

During the course of a chemical reaction **heat energy** is either given out or taken in. This heat energy is called **enthalpy** and this section introduces some important ideas about the **changes** in **enthalpy** which occur during a chemical reaction.

At the end of this section you should be able to . . .   ✔

Explain the terms *enthalpy* and *enthalpy change*.   ❑

Explain the terms, *exothermic*, *endothermic* and *activation energy*.   ❑

Draw potential energy diagrams for exothermic and endothermic reactions.   ❑

Calculate the enthalpy change and activation energy for exothermic and endothermic
reactions from potential energy diagrams.   ❑

Define the term *activated complex*.   ❑

Explain the formation of an activated complex using PE diagrams.   ❑

Explain how catalysts work by using PE diagrams.   ❑

Define the enthalpy changes of *combustion, solution* and *neutralisation*.   ❑

Write chemical equations for the enthalpy changes of *combustion, solution* and
neutralisation.   ❑

Describe how the enthalpy of combustion of an alcohol can be found by experiment
(*ppa*).   ❑

Calculate standard enthalpy changes of *combustion, solution* and *neutralisation*
from experimental data.   ❑

WORD LIST

The following words are introduced or used in this topic. You should be able to define, use and give examples of them where appropriate.

endothermic	enthalpy of neutralisation	kilojoules
enthalpy change	enthalpy of solution	potential energy diagrams
enthalpy of combustion	exothermic	standard enthalpy change

If you are not familiar with the meaning of any of these words, you should refer to the Glossary, where these words are defined.

ENTHALPY AND ENTHALPY CHANGES

Chemical reactions involve a change in energy which often results in the loss or gain of heat energy.

The **heat energy** stored in a substance is called its **Enthalpy** symbol — **H** — .

The **Enthalpy Change** — ΔH — during a reaction is the difference between the enthalpy of the reactants and the enthalpy of the products.

$$\Delta H \quad = \quad H_{(products)} \quad - \quad H_{(reactants)}$$

POTENTIAL ENERGY CHANGES

In terms of changes in enthalpy, reactions are either **exothermic** or **endothermic**. We can show the energy changes involved in both of these types of chemical reaction by using **potential energy** diagrams.

Exothermic Reactions

Changes which **give out heat energy** are called exothermic reactions.

The products have less enthalpy than the reactants and the temperature of the surroundings increases,
e.g. the combustion of fuels.

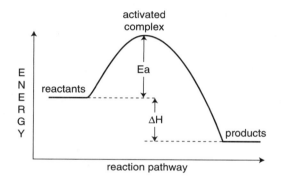

The **Ea** is **the activation energy**, which is needed to start the reaction.

ΔH is the amount of energy given out.

ΔH **is negative** for exothermic reactions.

Exothermic reactions are the most common type of enthalpy change.

Note   Some exothermic reactions, like the combustion of methane and other fuels, do not appear to occur at room temperature but require energy to start them. This is because, at room temperature, too few of the reactant molecules have sufficient energy to react when they collide. Striking a match supplies the required activation energy to get the chemical reaction going and it keeps going as energy is continually given out by the reaction.

Endothermic reactions

Changes which **absorb heat** energy are called **endothermic reactions**.

The products have more enthalpy than the reactants and the temperature of the surroundings decreases,
e.g. dissolving ammonium nitrate

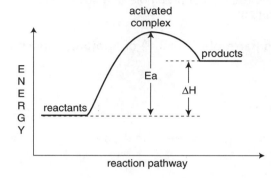

The **Ea** is the **activation energy**, which is needed to start the reaction.

ΔH is the amount of energy taken in.

ΔH **is positive** for Endothermic Reactions.

Note   In endothermic reactions the surroundings will cool down as energy is taken in when the products are formed. It may be necessary to continually supply energy to keep an endothermic reaction going.

Explaining Catalysts

We can show the effect of a **catalyst** by using a potential energy diagram.

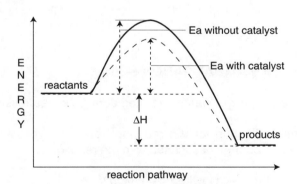

The presence of the catalyst **lowers the activation energy**, so that less energy is needed to form the activated complex and more of the reactant molecules will have sufficient energy to react on collision.
Notice that the catalyst has no effect on the overall enthalpy change, ΔH.

STANDARD ENTHALPY CHANGES

A **standard enthalpy change** defines the conditions under which the enthalpy change is measured and is used for comparison and in calculations.

The general definition for a standard enthalpy change is . . .

> "The heat energy liberated or absorbed by the reaction of one mole of a substance in its normal state at 1 atmosphere pressure and 298 K."

The units used for enthalpy changes are **joules per mole** ($J\ mol^{-1}$) or **kilojoules per mole** ($kJ\ mol^{-1}$).

STANDARD ENTHALPY OF COMBUSTION — ΔH_C

"The energy given out when 1 mole of a substance burns completely in excess oxygen, with all substances in their normal states,"

e.g.   The enthalpy of combustion of butane is the energy change associated with the reaction . .

$$C_4H_{10}(g) + \frac{13}{2}O_2(g) \rightarrow 4CO_2(g) + 5H_2O(l)$$
1 mole

STANDARD ENTHALPY OF SOLUTION — ΔH_S

"The energy released or absorbed when 1 mole of a substance dissolves completely in excess water,"

e.g.

$$Li\,F\,(s) + (aq) \rightarrow Li^+(aq) + F^-(aq)$$
1 mole

STANDARD ENTHALPY OF NEUTRALISATION — ΔH_N

"The energy released when 1 mole of water is formed during the neutralisation of an acid,"

e.g.   The enthalpy of neutralisation for the reaction between hydrochloric acid and sodium hydroxide is the energy change associated with the reaction . . .

$$HCl(aq) + NaOH(aq) \rightarrow NaCl(aq) + H_2O(l)$$
1 mole

CALCULATING ENTHALPY CHANGES BY EXPERIMENT

The **standard enthalpy change** of a chemical reaction can be found by experiment. This is usually done by measuring the temperature change, caused by the reaction, in a known mass of water.

The following equation can be used to calculate the change in heat energy.

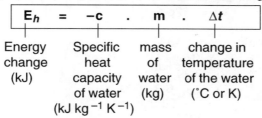

$$E_h \quad = \quad -c \quad . \quad m \quad . \quad \Delta t$$

| Energy change (kJ) | Specific heat capacity of water (kJ kg^{-1} K^{-1}) | mass of water (kg) | change in temperature of the water (°C or K) |

The **standard enthalpy change** can be found by calculating the change in heat energy which would be caused by one **mole** reacting.

Note   The specific heat capacity of water = 4.2 kJ kg^{-1} K^{-1}
         1 kJ = 1000 J and the density of water = 1 g cm^{-3} . (1kg l^{-1})

Example
It was found by experiment that when 2g of sodium hydroxide is added to 200 cm^3 of water the temperature rose from 18 °C to 20 °C. Assuming no heat losses, calculate the enthalpy of solution for sodium hydroxide.

Substituting in the equation
(note 200 cm^3 = 0.2 kg of water)

$$E_h = -c \cdot m \cdot \Delta t$$
$$= -4.2 \times 0.2 \times 2$$
$$= -1.68 \text{ kJ kg}$$

Formula mass of NaOH
= 23 + 16 + 1
= 40 amu

∴ 1 mole of NaOH = 40g

∴ 2g of NaOH dissolving   ⇔ −1.68 kJ

∴ 1g of NaOH dissolving   ⇔ $-\dfrac{1.68}{2}$
                      = −0.84 kJ

∴ 40g (1mole) of NaOH   ⇔ −40 × 0.84
                      = −25.6 kJ

∴ **ΔH_S of sodium hydroxide = −25.6 kJ mol^{-1}**

Enthalpy of combustion of an alcohol by experiment

Aim

To find the enthalpy of combustion of methanol.

Method

Use the apparatus set up as shown.

Measure the . . .

      mass of water,
      temperature change,
      change in mass of burner.

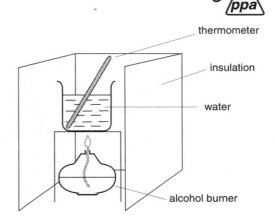

thermometer

insulation

water

alcohol burner

Sample Results

The temperature of 150 cm^3 of water rose by 10 °C when 0·29 g of methanol was burned.

Calculation

$$E_h = -c \cdot m \cdot \Delta t$$
$$\quad = -4\cdot2 \times 0\cdot15 \times 10$$
$$\quad = -6\cdot3 \text{ kJ}$$

Mass of 1 mole of methanol
$$CH_4O = 12 + 4 + 16$$
$$\quad = 32g$$

∴ Energy released by 0·29g of methanol $\quad \Leftrightarrow -6\cdot3 \text{ kJ}$

∴ Energy released by 1g of methanol $\quad \Leftrightarrow -\dfrac{6\cdot3}{0\cdot29} \text{ kJ}$

∴ Energy released by 32g of methanol $\quad \Leftrightarrow -32 \times \dfrac{6\cdot3}{0\cdot29}$

$$\quad = -695\cdot2 \text{ kJ}$$

∴ ΔH_C **methanol** $= -695\cdot2 \text{ kJ mol}^{-1}$

Experimental error — The values of enthalpies of combustion, found by experiment, will always be lower than they should be, as we assume no heat losses but some energy must be lost to the apparatus and surroundings.

PATTERNS IN THE PERIODIC TABLE

Since its invention in 1869, the **Periodic Table** has helped us to understand and explain the chemistry of the known elements.

In this section we look at how the Periodic Table was devised and how the positions of elements can be used as a guide to their properties.

At the end of this section you should be able to . . .   ✔

State some facts about the discovery of the elements.   ❐
Describe how the Periodic Table was originally based on atomic masses and properties.   ❐
Understand that there are variations in the m.pt., b.pt. and density of the elements,
    across a period and down a group.   ❐
Explain the term *periodicity* by referring to the elements' properties.   ❐
Explain the trend in atomic volume across a period and down a group.   ❐
Define and write equations for the first, second, third, etc., *ionisation energies* of an
    element.   ❐
Explain trend in ionisation energy across a period and down a group.   ❐
Explain the difference between the first, second, third, etc., *ionisation energies* of an
    element.   ❐
Define and use the term *electronegativity*.   ❐
Explain the trend in electronegativity across a period and down a group.   ❐

WORD LIST

The following words are introduced or used in this topic. You should be able to define, use and give examples of them where appropriate.

alkali metal	element	noble gas
atomic volume	group	period
electron arrangement	halogen	Periodic Table
electronegativity	ionisation enthalpy	screening effect

If you are not familiar with the meaning of any of these words, you should refer to the Glossary, where these words are defined.

DISCOVERY OF THE ELEMENTS

An **element** is a substance which cannot be broken down into a simpler substance as it is made up of only **one kind of atom**.

There are **91 natural elements**, which make up all the different matter in the universe, and about 20 others which have been man-made.

A **compound** is a substance made up of two or more elements joined together.

There are **millions** of different **compounds** in the world.

Many elements, like **gold, silver, copper** and **sulphur**, have been known since **ancient times** as they are found **uncombined** in the earth's crust. Elements like **lead, iron** and **tin** were discovered when man learned to use fire and heat to **decompose** their compounds and extract the elements. The very reactive metals, like **potassium, sodium** and **lithium**, are made by **electrolysis** of their molten ores, so they were only discovered when we were able to make and use electricity.

By the end of the 19th century chemists had identified over 60 elements and the search had begun to make sense of their different properties.

PATTERNS IN THE PERIODIC TABLE

The **Periodic Table** was invented in 1869 by Dimitri Mendeleyev, a Russian chemist. Mendeleyev noted that if the elements were placed in order of increasing **atomic mass**, their properties, like **melting point**, **boiling point** and **density**, showed a **periodic nature**. He then arranged the elements by putting those with similar properties below each other in **groups**. To make his classification work, Mendeleyev made a few changes to the order and left gaps for elements yet to be discovered. He even predicted the properties of these unknown elements with some accuracy.

Dimitri Mendeleyev

The modern **Periodic Table** is based on the element's **atomic number**.

Consider the graph of the **melting points** against **atomic number** which is shown below.

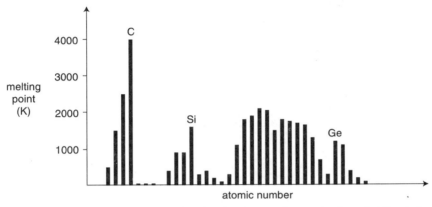

The regular rise and fall of the graph clearly shows the typical **periodic nature** of the property. Mendeleyev used the periodicity of the melting points and other properties of the elements to devise the **Periodic Table**.

The **Periodic Table** was used to show **similarities** in properties within **groups** and **trends** in properties **across periods** and **down groups**.

The explanation of these trends and similarities only became possible, however, after we gained a better understanding of **atomic structure** and **bonding**.

ATOMIC NUMBER AND ELECTRON ARRANGEMENTS

The modern Periodic Table is based on **increasing atomic number**.

Consider the electron arrangements of the first 20 elements . . .

	Groups							
	I	II	III	IV	V	VI	VII	VIII
	H							He
	1							2
	Li	Be	B	C	N	O	F	Ne
Periods	2,1	2,2	2,3	2,4	2,5	2,6	2,7	2,8
	Na	Mg	Al	Si	P	S	Cl	Ar
	2,8,1	2,8,2	2,8,3	2,8,4	2,8,5	2,8,6	2,8,7	2,8,8
	K	Ca						
	2,8,8,1	2,8,8,2						

As we go across a **period** the **nuclear charge** and the number of **outer electrons** increase.

As we go down a **group** the number of **electron shells** or **energy levels** increases but the number of **outer electrons** stays the same.

TRENDS IN ATOMIC VOLUME

The trend in atomic volume is . . .

Across a period the **atomic volume decreases** as the nuclear charge increases attracting the outer electrons closer to the nucleus.

Down a group the **atomic volume increases** as an extra electron shell is added.

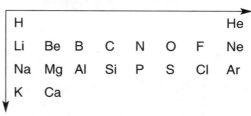

TRENDS IN IONISATION ENERGY

Definition . . .

> *"The **ionisation energy** is the energy absorbed **when 1 mole of electrons** is **removed** from a **mole of atoms** in the **gaseous state**."*

The trend in ionisation energy is ...

Across a period **ionisation energy increases** as the nuclear charge increases, attracting the outer electrons more strongly.

Down a group the **ionisation energy decreases** as the outer electrons are further away from the nucleus and the screening effect of the inner electron shell means the attraction for the outer electrons is less strong.

H							He
Li	Be	B	C	N	O	F	Ne
Na	Mg	Al	Si	P	S	Cl	Ar
K	Ca						

Note   The **1st ionisation energy** is the energy needed to remove the first mole of electrons and the **2nd ionisation energy** is the energy needed to remove the second mole of electrons, etc.,

e.g. The ionisation energies for Magnesium are . . .

1st	$Mg(g)$	$\rightarrow$	$Mg^+(g)$	$+ e$	744	$kJ\,mol^{-1}$
2nd	$Mg^+(g)$	$\rightarrow$	$Mg^{2+}(g)$	$+ e$	1460	$kJ\,mol^{-1}$
3rd	$Mg^{2+}(g)$	$\rightarrow$	$Mg^{3+}(g)$	$+ e$	7750	$kJ\,mol^{-1}$

Note   Successive ionisation energies increase as the atom becomes more positive.
There is a large jump in ionisation energy when the electron to be removed comes from a new shell, closer to the nucleus,
e.g. between 2nd and 3rd ionisation energy for magnesium.

TREND IN ELECTRONEGATIVITY

Definition . . .

> *"**Electronegativity** is a measure of an atom's **attraction for electrons** in a bond."*

The trend in electronegativity is ...

Across a period, **electronegativity increases** as the nuclear charge increases, attracting the electrons more strongly.

Electronegativity decreases down a group as the bonding electrons are further away from the nucleus and the screening effect of the inner electron shell means the attraction for the bonding electrons is less strong.

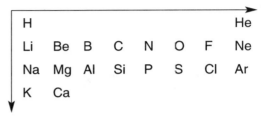

The values for electronegativity can be found in the data book and they are used in the next section as a guide to bonding type.

BONDING STRUCTURE AND PROPERTIES

Bonding is of fundamental importance in chemistry, since we must understand how atoms are held together before we can explain the simplest **chemical reaction** or **physical change**.

At the end of this section you should be able to . . .   ✔

Explain why atoms form bonds.   ❏
Explain how *metallic* and *covalent bonds* are formed in elements.   ❏
Explain how *covalent, polar-covalent* and *ionic bonds* are formed in compounds.   ❏
Explain all types of bond in terms of electrostatic forces.   ❏
Explain how the type of bond formed is affected by electronegativity.   ❏
Describe where and how *Van der Waals' forces* arise.   ❏
Explain the relative strength of Van der Waals' forces.   ❏
Explain what is meant by a *polar molecule* and a *permanent dipole*.   ❏
Explain the difference between polar and non-polar molecules.   ❏
Describe where and how hydrogen bonds arise.   ❏
Describe the relative strengths of different *intermolecular forces*.   ❏
Describe the structure of both ionic and metallic solids.   ❏
Explain the difference between *covalent molecules* and *networks*.   ❏
Describe the bonding and structure in each of the elements 1 to 20.   ❏
Describe, with examples, the three bonding structures of compounds.   ❏
Relate bonding and structure to hardness, melting and boiling points.   ❏
Explain the difference in boiling point between polar and non-polar substances of similar
mass.   ❏
Describe how different substances can conduct electricity.   ❏
Relate bonding and structure to solubility in different solvents.   ❏
Explain how hydrogen bonds can influence b.pt/m.pt., density, viscosity and solubility.   ❏
Explain the properties and uses of graphite, diamond and silicon carbide.   ❏
Describe *Fullerenes* and some of the current research into them and their uses.   ❏

WORD LIST

The following words are introduced or used in this topic. You should be able to define, use and give examples of them where appropriate.

compound	intermolecular bonding	non-polar molecule
covalent bonding	ionic bonding	non-polar solvent
diamond	ionic lattice	polar molecule
diatomic molecule	lattice structure	polar solvent
dipole	metallic bonding	polar-covalent bonding
electrostatic forces	metallic lattice	polar-polar attractions
fullerenes	molecular structure	Van der Waals' forces
graphite	monatomic	
hydrogen bonds	network structure	

If you are not familiar with the meaning of any of these words, you should refer to the Glossary, where these words are defined.

THE FORMATION OF BONDS

Bonds are **electrostatic forces** (attractions between positive and negative charges) which hold atoms together.
Atoms form bonds to become more **stable**.

When bonds are formed, electrons can be lost, gained or shared, as the atoms try to attain a stable electron arrangement like the **noble gases**,
        i.e.   He 2;   Ne 2,8;   Ar 2,8,8;   Kr 2,8,18,8;   Xe 2,8,18,18,8.
The noble gases are a group of elements which do not form bonds readily as they are already very stable.

TYPES OF BONDING AND STRUCTURE

The **type of bond** formed in a substance depends on the nature of the elements involved and their positions in the Periodic Table.

The **electronegativity** values of the elements can be a useful guide to bonding type.

Metallic or **covalent bonds** are formed in **elements**.
Polar-covalent or **ionic bonds** are formed in **compounds**.

METALLIC BONDING

Metallic bonding occurs between the atoms of **metal elements**, which are found on the left hand side of the Periodic Table.

Metals have little attraction for their outer **electrons** which are free to move, **delocalised**, throughout a **lattice structure** of positive metal ions.

Metallic lattice

The **metallic lattice** is held together by **electrostatic forces** of attraction between the millions of positive ions and their delocalised outer electrons.

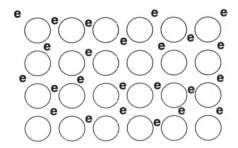

COVALENT AND POLAR-COVALENT BONDING

Covalent bonding occurs in **non-metal elements**, which are found on the right hand side of the Periodic Table.

Non-metal elements have a great attraction for their outer electrons and form a bond by **equal sharing of electrons** between atoms, e.g.

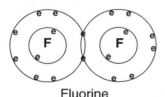

Fluorine

Counting the shared electrons, the atoms have an electron arrangement like a noble gas.

Polar-covalent bonding is similar to covalent bonding but is formed in compounds between different non-metal elements so the atoms have **slightly different electronegativities**, attraction for electrons.

In **Polar-covalent bonds** the electrons are **unequally shared**,

e.g.

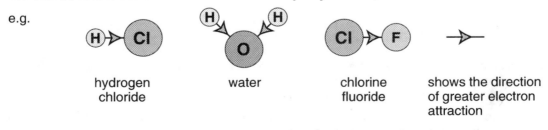

| hydrogen chloride | water | chlorine fluoride | shows the direction of greater electron attraction |

The atom with the largest electronegativity has the greatest attraction for electrons.

The atoms in a **covalent** and **polar-covalent bond** are held together by **electrostatic forces** of attraction between the positively charged nuclei and negatively charged shared electrons.

Covalent and polar-covalent substances are usually made up of **discrete molecules**, but a few have giant **network structures**.

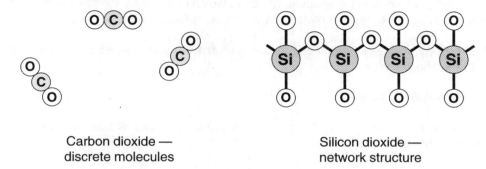

Carbon dioxide —
discrete molecules

Silicon dioxide —
network structure

IONIC BONDING

Ionic bonds are formed between **metal** and **non-metal atoms**, with a **large difference in electronegativity**.

Losing and gaining electrons forms **ions** with electron arrangements like the noble gases, e.g.

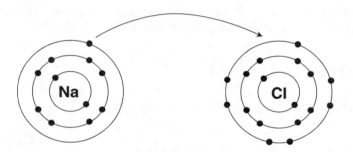

Metal atoms, with low electronegativity, **lose electrons** to form **positive ions**,
e.g.   Na $\rightarrow$ Na^+ + e
       (2,8,1)   (2,8)
Non-metals atoms, with high electronegativity, **gain electrons** to form **negative ions**,
e.g.   Cl + e $\rightarrow$ Cl^-
         (2,8,7)   (2,8,8)

In both cases a noble gas electron arrangement is attained. The oppositely charged **ions** are held together by **electrostatic forces** and form a regular arrangement which is called a **lattice structure**.

In ionic compounds we call this an **Ionic lattice**.

BONDING BETWEEN MOLECULES

Apart from the covalent and polar-covalent bonds which hold atoms together in molecules, there are attractive forces between the molecules which can affect their properties.

These attractions between molecules are called **intermolecular forces** or **bonds**, and they can arise in three different ways.

VAN DER WAALS' FORCES

The weakest form of intermolecular bonding is called **Van der Waals' forces**, and it exists between all atoms and molecules.

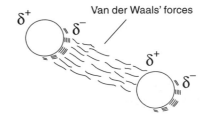

Van der Waals' forces are caused by uneven distributions of electrons. The atom or molecule gets slightly charged ends and this induces an opposite charge in neighbouring atoms or molecules.

The **oppositely charged** ends **attract** each other.

(δ^+ means slightly positive and δ^- means slightly negative.)

The relative strength of the Van der Waals' forces depend on the size of the atoms or molecules. Van der Waals' forces increase with increasing atomic and molecular size.

POLAR-POLAR ATTRACTIONS

Some **polar-covalent** substances contain **polar molecules**.

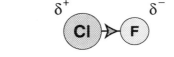

A **polar molecule** is one which has permanently charged ends (δ^+ and δ^-) called a **permanent dipole**.

The element with the greatest electronegativity will attract the electrons more and become δ^-.

Polar-polar attractions are the intermolecular force of attraction between the oppositely charged ends of the polar molecules.

Polar-polar attractions are stronger than **Van der Waals' forces**.

e.g.

Note Not all substances with Polar covalent bonds will have "polar molecules", this depends on the shape of the molecules. A symmetrical structure may have polar-covalent bonds but no charged ends.

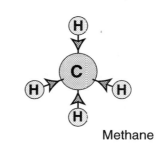

Methane

HYDROGEN BONDS

A strong intermolecular force of attraction is found in polar-covalent substances with **very "polar" molecules**.

This intermolecular force is called **hydrogen bonding**, as in polar-polar attractions, the oppositely charged ends of the molecules attract each other, e.g., hydrogen fluoride.

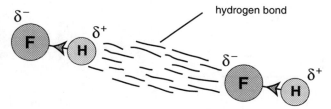

Hydrogen bonds are usually found in molecules where hydrogen is bonded to very electronegative atoms like fluorine, oxygen or nitrogen, which have a great attraction for electrons.

Other examples of substances which have hydrogen bonding are . . .
        water, **ammonia**, **alkanoic acids** and **alkanols**.

Hydrogen bonds are stronger than polar-polar attractions and Van der Waals' forces but weaker than covalent bonds.

BONDING AND THE PROPERTIES OF ELEMENTS 1 TO 20

Elements can be split into four main groups, depending on their bonding, structure and properties.

Monatomic or Noble Gases

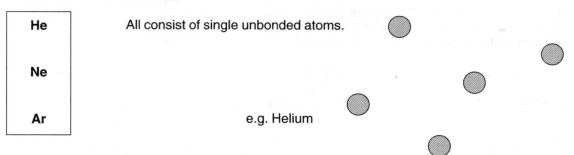

| He |
| Ne |
| Ar |

All consist of single unbonded atoms.

e.g. Helium

All gases with very **low densities, m.pts.** and **b.pts.**
Only Van der Waals' forces between the atoms.
Non conductors of electricity as no freely moving charged particles.

M.pts. and b.pts. increase with increasing atomic size as the Van der Waals' forces increase.

e.g..   He   m.pt.   −272 °C
         Ne   m.pt.   −249 °C   increasing
         Ar   m.pt.   −189 °C   atomic size
         Kr   m.pt.   −157 °C

Covalent Molecular

H		
N	**O**	**F**
P	**S**	**Cl**

All consist of discrete molecules of varying molecular size.

e.g. Nitrogen (N_2)

e.g. Phosphorous (P_4)

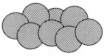

e.g. Sulphur (S_8)

Gases and solids with **fairly low densities**, **m.pts** and **b.pts**.
Only Van der Waals' forces between the molecules, m.pts. and b.pts. increase with increasing molecular size.
Non conductors of electricity as no freely moving charged particles.

Covalent Network

B	**C**
Si	

All have giant network structures containing millions of atoms.

All solids with **very high densities**, **m.pts**. and **b.pts**.
Lots of strong bonds to break up lattice structure.
Non-conductors of electricity (except graphite).

For example, carbon exists in two main forms . . .

Graphite

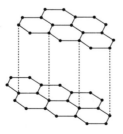

3 bonds per atom
layer structure
structure

Conductors of electricity due to delocalised electrons between the layers.
Slippery, layers break away easily, used as lubricant, pencils, etc.

Diamond

4 bonds per atom
tetrahedral
structure

Non-conductor of electricity as all outer electrons are involved in bonding.
Hardest natural substance as many strong bonds to break, used for drills, cutting glass, etc.

Note   **Fullerenes** are a recently developed form of carbon, made up of large spherical molecules, the commonest containing 60 carbon atoms. Work on fullerenes has led to the development of tiny tubes made up of carbon. These so called "nanotubes" could have many important applications, and the search for uses continues.

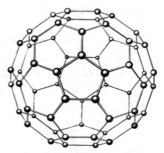

buckminsterfullerene

Metallic Lattice Structure

Li	Be	
Na	Mg	Al
K	Ca	

All have metallic lattice structures.

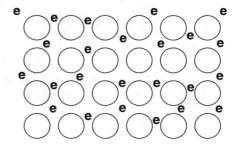

All solids with **high densities**, **m.pts**. and **b.pts**.
Closely packed lattice structure with lots of strong bonds to break.
Conductors of electricity, when solid or liquid, due to the delocalised outer electrons, which are free to move.
When electricity passes through a metal no chemical change occurs.

BONDING AND PROPERTIES OF COMPOUNDS

Compounds can be split into three main groups, depending on their bonding, structure and properties.

● **Ionic Lattice Structures**

All **ionic compounds** are **solids** at room temperature and have **high melting points and boiling points**. This is due to the lattice structure as many strong bonds need to be broken to change state.

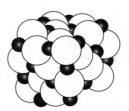

Ionic compounds **conduct electricity** when **dissolved in water** or when **molten** as the ions are free to move.

During the **electrolysis** of ionic solutions or melts, a chemical change occurs at the electrodes.

They **do not conduct** when **solid** as the ions are "locked" in the lattice and cannot move to carry the current.

● **Covalent Network Structures**

Covalent network structures have **very high melting points and boiling points** as many strong bonds need to be broken to change state.
Covalent network structures can also be **very hard**.

e.g.

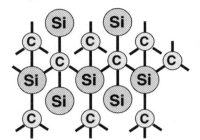

Silicon Carbide has a tetrahedral lattice structure like diamond, it has a very high melting point and is used as an abrasive.

Covalent network structures are usually **non-conductors of electricity** as they have no freely moving charged particles.

● **Covalent Molecular Structures**

Covalent molecular structures usually have **low melting points and boiling points** as there is little attraction between their molecules,

e.g. carbon dioxide m.pt. –57 ˚C.

However, compounds with **polar molecules** may have **slightly higher m.pts. and b.pts.** than compounds with non-polar molecules.
This is due to **polar-polar attractions**. Consider the two polar molecules below.

e.g.   Iodine Chloride   and   Bromine
              I—Cl   Br—Br
           b.pt. 97 ˚C   b.pt. 59 ˚C

Note   We must compare compounds of similar molecular mass so that Van der Waals' forces will be equivalent.

When **hydrogen bonds** are present, the compound will have a **much higher m.pt. and b.pt.** than other compounds of similar molecular size,

e.g. **Ethanol**
Molecular mass = 46 amu
b.pt. = 80 °C

$$H-\underset{\underset{H}{|}}{\overset{\overset{H}{|}}{C}}-\underset{\underset{H}{|}}{\overset{\overset{H}{|}}{C}}-O^{\diagup H}$$

Strong hydrogen bonds due to very polar molecules

Ether
Molecular mass = 46 amu
b.pt. = −23 °C

$$H-\underset{\underset{H}{|}}{\overset{\overset{H}{|}}{C}}-O-\underset{\underset{H}{|}}{\overset{\overset{H}{|}}{C}}-H$$

No hydrogen bonds as non-polar molecules

Consider the trend in boiling points of the hydrides of groups 4, 5, 6 and 7.
Some of the b.pts. seem out of place.
In groups 5, 6 and 7 the first hydride has a boiling point much higher than would be expected from its molecular size.

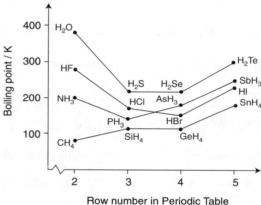

Row number in Periodic Table

This is because they have the most polar molecules and strong hydrogen bonds hold them together. More energy is needed to separate their molecules in changing from a liquid to a gas.
This is not the case with group 4 hydrides as they don't have polar molecules due to their symmetrical structure.

HYDOGEN BONDING AND THE PROPERTIES OF WATER

Water has some unusual properties caused by the **hydrogen bonding** between its molecules.

The **density** of ice is less than water

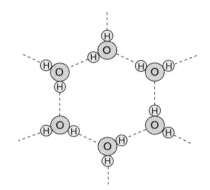

As matter is cooled, it normally contracts and becomes more dense.

However, as water freezes it expands because the strong hydrogen bonds between the molecules form an open lattice structure. The solid ice is less dense than the liquid and ice floats on water.

Water molecules in ice

The **high viscosity** and **surface tension** of water is also caused by the presence of hydrogen bonding.

BONDING, SOLUBILITY AND SOLUTIONS

Ionic lattices and **polar-covalent molecular** compounds tend to be . . .

● **soluble** in **water** and other **polar solvents**, due to the attraction between the opposite charges,

● **insoluble** in **non-polar solvents**, as there is no attraction between the ions and the solvent molecules,

   e.g.   When ionic compounds dissolve in water the lattice is broken up the ions become surrounded by water molecules.

The negative ions are attracted to the positive ends of the polar water molecules.

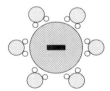

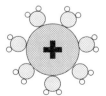

The positive ions are attracted to the negative ends of the polar water molecules.

Non-polar covalent molecular substances tend to be . . .

● **soluble** in **non-polar solvents** like hexane or carbon tetrachloride.

● **insoluble** in **water** and other **polar solvents** as there are no charged ends to be attracted.

AVOGADRO AND THE MOLE

This section revises and develops the **mole** concept and introduces its use in different types of chemical **calculations** including calculations involving, masses, number of particles, excess and volumes of gases.

At the end of this section you should be able to . . .   ✔

Complete calculations relating moles to masses and masses to moles.   ❏
Complete calculations to find the concentration of a solution and the mass of solute
    dissolved.   ❏
Define a mole of a substance in terms of the Avogadro constant.   ❏
Relate the number of formula units in different substances to the number of moles
    present.   ❏
Explain the term "molar gas volume" and state its units.   ❏
Calculate the molar gas volume from experimental data.   ❏
Complete calculations relating moles to volume and volume to moles.   ❏
Complete calculations involving moles, masses, volumes and numbers of particles.   ❏
Complete calculations to find the amount of reactants or product involved in a
    chemical reaction.   ❏
Complete calculations to find the reactant in excess.   ❏
Complete calculations to find the volumes of gases in a reaction.   ❏

WORD LIST

The following words are introduced or used in this topic. You should be able to define, use and give examples of them where appropriate.

Avogadro's constant   excess reactant   molar gas volume
concentration   formula unit   mole

If you are not familiar with the meaning of any of these words, you should refer to the Glossary, where these words are defined.

THE MOLE AND MASS

A **mole** (mol) of a substance is defined as the **formula mass** in **grams**, also known as the **gram formula mass**.

Example 1

What is the mass of 2·5 moles of solid sodium hydroxide?

	Formula	=	NaOH
∴	Formula mass	=	23 + 16 + 1
		=	40 amu
∴	1 mole of sodium hydroxide	⇔	40 g
∴	2·5 moles	⇔	2·5 × 40
		=	**100 g**

Example 2

How many moles are in 4·9 g of sulphuric acid?

	Formula	=	H_2SO_4
∴	Formula mass	=	$(2 \times 1) + 32 + (16 \times 4)$
		=	98 amu
∴	98g of sulphuric acid	⇔	1 mole
∴	1g	⇔	$\frac{1}{98}$ moles
∴	4·9 g	⇔	$4·9 \times \frac{1}{98}$
		=	**0·05 moles**

MOLES AND SOLUTIONS

In chemistry the **concentration** of a solution is usually measured in **moles per litre** (mol l^{-1})

The following equation can be used in calculations involving concentrations.

$$\boxed{Nm = C \times V}$$

Where **Nm** = number of moles of solute (mol)
 C = concentration of solution (mol l^{-1})
 V = volume of solution in litres (l)

Example 3

How many moles of sodium hydroxide are dissolved in 200 cm^3 of 0·5 mol l^{-1} solution?

$$Nm = C \times V$$
$$= 0·5 \times 0·2^* \qquad (\text{*Remember volume is in litres})$$
$$= \mathbf{0·1\ moles}$$

Example 4

What is the concentration of a solution of sulphuric acid containing 0·2 mol of acid in 100 cm^3 of solution?

$$Nm = C \times V$$
$$C = \frac{Nm}{V}$$
$$= \frac{0·2}{0·1}$$
$$= \mathbf{2·0\ mol\ } l^{-1}$$

Example 5

What mass of solid sodium carbonate is required to make up 100 cm^3 of 0·25 mol l^{-1} solution?

Formula	=	Na_2CO_3
Formula mass	=	$(23 \times 2) + 12 + (16 \times 3)$
	=	106 amu
∴ 1 mole	⇔	106g
Now **Nm**	=	**C × V**
	=	0·25 × 0.1
∴ moles of solute	=	0·025 moles
∴ mass of solute	=	0·025 × 106
	=	**2·65 g**

MOLES AND NUMBER OF PARTICLES

A **mole** of a substance always contains the **same number** of "**formula units**" as a mole of any other substance.

This number is called **The Avogadro constant**.

$$\boxed{\textbf{The Avogadro constant} = \mathbf{6 \cdot 02 \times 10^{23} \ mol^{-1}}}$$

The "formula units" may be atoms, or molecules or even formulae, depending on the type of substance,

e.g.

64g of Cu metal contains $6 \cdot 02 \times 10^{23}$ Cu atoms	18g of H_2O liquid contains $6 \cdot 02 \times 10^{23}$ H_2O molecules	40g of NaOH solid contains $6 \cdot 02 \times 10^{23}$ NaOH formulae

This also means that **equimolar amounts** of different substances will contain the **same number of formula units**.

Example 6

Which of the following contain the same number of atoms?

A   20 g of neon gas.
B   8 g of oxygen gas.
C   14 g of nitrogen.
D   8·5 g of ammonia.

Calculate the number of moles of each of the gases in the question.

A   1 mole of Ne   = 20 g   ∴ 20 g = 1 mole of Ne
B   1 mole of O_2 = 32 g   ∴   8 g = 0·25 moles of O_2
C   1 mole of N_2 = 28 g   ∴ 14 g = 0·5 moles of N_2
D   1 mole of NH_3 = 17 g   ∴ 8·5 g = 0·5 moles of NH_3

Now calculate the number of moles of atoms in each.

A   Ne is monatomic, 1 atom   ∴   1 mole of Ne = 1 mole of atoms
B O_2 is diatomic, 2 atoms   ∴   0·25 moles of O_2 = 0·5 moles of atoms
C N_2 is diatomic, 2 atoms   ∴   0·5 moles of N_2 = 1 mole of atoms
D NH_3 contains 4 atoms   ∴   0·5 moles of NH_3 = 2 moles of atoms

∴   **A and C contain the same number of atoms.**

Example 7

How many molecules are in 16g of oxygen gas?

The calculation must change . . . **mass $\Leftrightarrow$ number**

1 mole of O_2 = 32g
1 mole of O_2 = $6 \cdot 02 \times 10^{23}$ formula units or molecules

$\therefore$ 32g of oxygen $\Leftrightarrow$ $6 \cdot 02 \times 10^{23}$ molecules

$\therefore$ 1g of oxygen $\Leftrightarrow$ $\dfrac{6 \cdot 02 \times 10^{23}}{32}$ molecules

$\therefore$ 16g of oxygen $\Leftrightarrow$ $16 \times \dfrac{6 \cdot 02 \times 10^{23}}{32}$ molecules

$$= 3 \cdot 01 \times 10^{23} \textbf{ molecules of oxygen}$$

Example 8

How many atoms of hydrogen are in 8 g of methane?

The calculation must change . . . **mass $\Leftrightarrow$ number**

1 mole of CH_4 = 16g
1 mole of CH_4 = $6 \cdot 02 \times 10^{23}$ formula units or molecules

$\therefore$ 16g of methane $\Leftrightarrow$ $6 \cdot 02 \times 10^{23}$ molecules of methane

Now 1 molecule of CH_4 = 4 atoms of hydrogen

$\therefore$ 16g of methane $\Leftrightarrow$ $4 \times 6 \cdot 02 \times 10^{23}$ atoms of hydrogen

$\therefore$ 1g of methane $\Leftrightarrow$ $\dfrac{4 \times 6 \cdot 02 \times 10^{23}}{16}$ atoms of hydrogen

$\therefore$ 8g of methane $\Leftrightarrow$ $8 \times \dfrac{4 \times 6 \cdot 02 \times 10^{23}}{16}$ atoms of hydrogen

$$= 1 \cdot 204 \times 10^{24} \textbf{ atoms of hydrogen}$$

THE MOLE AND GAS VOLUMES

It can be shown that, under the same conditions of temperature and pressure, a mole of any gas will have the same volume.

This is called the **molar gas volume** and it is usually measured in litres per mole ($l\,mol^{-1}$).

The molar gas volume can be calculated from experimental results and used in calculations involving gas, volumes, masses and densities.

Example 9

A 3·5 litre container which weighed 123·0 g empty had a mass of 129·2 g when filled with carbon dioxide at 25 °C. What is the molar gas volume of carbon dioxide at this temperature?

	Formula	=	CO_2
∴	Formula mass	=	$12 + (2 \times 16)$
		=	44 amu
∴	1 mole of CO_2	⇔	44 g
	Mass of container + CO_2	=	129·2 g
	Mass of container empty	=	123·0 g
∴	Mass of CO_2	=	6·2 g
∴	6·2g of CO_2	⇔	3·5 litres
∴	1g of CO_2	⇔	$\dfrac{3\cdot5}{6\cdot2}$ litres
∴	44g of CO_2 (1 mole)	⇔	$44 \times \dfrac{3\cdot5}{6\cdot2}$
		=	24·8 litres
∴	**The molar gas volume**	=	**24·8 litres mol^{-1}**

Example 10

If 100 cm^3 of a gaseous element was found to have a mass of 0·1784 g, calculate the formula mass and suggest a possible name for the gas (molar gas volume is 22·4 litres mol^{-1}).

	Now 100 cm^3 of the gas	$\Leftrightarrow$	0·1784 g
$\therefore$	1 cm^3 of the gas	$\Leftrightarrow$	$\dfrac{0·1784}{100}$ g
$\therefore$	22 400 cm^3 of the gas	$\Leftrightarrow$	$22\,400 \times \dfrac{0·1784}{100}$
	(1 mole)	=	40 g (to nearest whole number)
$\therefore$	**Formula mass**	=	**40. The gas could be argon.**

● In some calculations density, a measure of mass to volume, is used.

$$\boxed{\textbf{Density} \ = \ \frac{\textbf{Mass}}{\textbf{Volume}}}$$

The units of density are usually $g\,l^{-1}$ or $g\,cm^{-3}$

Example 11

If the molar gas volume of oxygen is 21·8 litres mol^{-1} at room temperature, what is its density of oxygen at this temperature?

The required mole relationship is . . .

	mass	$\Leftrightarrow$	**volume**
	1 mole of O_2	$\Leftrightarrow$	21·8 litres
	Formula mass of O_2	$\Leftrightarrow$	2×16 = 32 amu
$\therefore$	1 mole of O_2	$\Leftrightarrow$	32g
$\therefore$	32g of O_2	$\Leftrightarrow$	21·8 litres
	Now Density	=	$\dfrac{Mass}{Volume}$
$\therefore$	Density of oxygen	=	$\dfrac{32}{21·8}$
		=	**1·47 g l^{-1}**

THINKING ABOUT MOLE RELATIONSHIPS

Calculations in chemistry often involve relationships of **moles**, **masses**, **numbers** or **volumes**. Thinking about the **mole relationship** required to answer the question is a good way of starting these types of calculation.

Examples of mole relationship are . . .   **moles**   ⇔   **volume**
                                            volume   ⇔   **number**
                                            number   ⇔   **mass**
                                            etc.

Example 12

A pupil collected a 50 cm^3 sample of oxygen gas. If the molar gas volume is 24 litres mol^{-1}, how many atoms of oxygen did he collect?

In this question the required mole relationship is . . .
                    volume   ⇔   **number**
                (given in question)   (asked to find)

Now   1 mole of oxygen   ⇔   24 litres = 24 000 cm^3
and   1 mole of oxygen   ⇔ 6.02×10^{23} formula units or molecules
Now   **volume**   ⇔   **number**
∴   24 000 cm^3 of oxygen   ⇔ 6.02×10^{23} molecules
∴   1 cm^3 of oxygen   ⇔ $\dfrac{6.02 \times 10^{23}}{24\,000}$ molecules
∴   50 cm^3 of oxygen   ⇔ $50 \times \dfrac{6.02 \times 10^{23}}{24\,000}$ molecules
                                 = 1.25×10^{21} molecules

Now 1 molecule of oxygen (O_2) contains 2 atoms
∴   50 cm^3 of oxygen   ⇔ $2 \times 1.25 \times 10^{21}$
                                 = $\mathbf{2.5 \times 10^{21}}$ **atoms**

Example 13

What mass of carbon dioxide will contain 2.5×10^{22} molecules of the gas?

In this question the required mole relationship is . . .
                    number   ⇔   **mass**
                (given in question)   (asked to find)

Now   1 mole of CO_2 = 6.02×10^{23} molecules
and   1 mole of CO_2 = $12 + (2 \times 16) = 44$ g
Now   **number**   ⇔   **mass**
∴ 6.02×10^{23} molecules ⇔   44 g carbon dioxide
∴   1 molecule   ⇔ $\dfrac{44}{6.02 \times 10^{23}}$ g
∴ 2.5×10^{22} molecules ⇔ $2.5 \times 10^{22} \times \dfrac{44}{6.02 \times 10^{23}}$ g
                                     = $\mathbf{1.83}$ **g**

MOLES AND BALANCED CHEMICAL EQUATIONS

Balanced chemical equations can be used to calculate the amounts of reactant or product in a chemical reaction, by the following stages.

Stage 1 Find the **balanced chemical equation**.
Stage 2 Find the **mole ratios** of substances in question.
Stage 3 Change the **units** (mol, g, l, etc.) as required.
Stage 4 **Solve** problem by simple proportion.

When one reactant in a chemical reaction is used up, the reaction stops, any other reactant left is said to be in **excess**.

Balanced equations can also be used to calculate the reactant in excess.

Example 14

What volume of carbon dioxide would be produced when 5g of calcium carbonate reacted with excess hydrochloric acid?
(molar gas volume = 22.4 litres mol^{-1})

1. Balanced equation. $CaCO_3 + 2HCl \rightarrow CaCl_2 + H_2O + CO_2$

2. Mole ratios   1 mole $CaCO_3$ $\Leftrightarrow$ 1 mole CO_2

3. Change the units $40 + 12 + (16 \times 3)$
                            $= 100g$ $\Leftrightarrow$ 22·4 litres
                            $\therefore$ 100g $CaCO_3$ $\Leftrightarrow$ 22·4 litres CO_2

4. Solve problem $\therefore$ 1g $CaCO_3$ $\Leftrightarrow$ $\dfrac{22·4}{100}$

                            $\therefore$ 5g $CaCO_3$ $\Leftrightarrow$ $5 \times \dfrac{22·4}{100}$

                                                        $=$ **1·12 litres CO_2**

Example 15

Which reactant is in excess when 0·25g of magnesium is added to 100 cm^3 of 0·1 mol l^{-1} hydrochloric acid?

First calculate the number of moles of each reactant.

Moles of **Mg**   Moles of **HCl**
1 mole Mg $\Leftrightarrow$ 24g Nm = $C \times V$

$\therefore$ 0·25g Mg $\Leftrightarrow$ $\dfrac{0·25}{24}$ $= 0·1 \times 0·1$

                    $= 0·01$ moles $= 0·01$ moles

Then find the mole ratio from the equation for the reaction
$Mg + 2HCl \rightarrow MgCl_2 + H_2$
$\therefore$ 1 mole Mg $\Leftrightarrow$ 2 moles HCl
$\therefore$ 0·005 moles Mg $\Leftrightarrow$ 0·01 moles HCl

$\therefore$ **Magnesium is in excess and all the HCl will be used up.**

VOLUMES OF GASES INVOLVED IN REACTIONS

Equal volumes of **gases** contain **equal numbers** of **formula units**.

> e.g. The number of molecules in 1 litre of methane will be the same as the number of atoms in 1 litre of argon, etc.

● We can calculate the **volumes of gases** reacting and produced in a **chemical reaction** by using the **balanced chemical equation** to tell us the **ratio** of the **volumes** of the gases involved.

Example 16

What is the final gas composition and volume when 20 cm^3 of butane is sparked with 130 cm^3 of oxygen, if all measurements are made at 125 °C?

The chemical equation . . .

$$C_4H_{10}(g) \quad + \quad \frac{13}{2}O_2(g) \quad \rightarrow \quad 4CO_2(g) \quad + \quad 5H_2O(g)$$

∴ *ratio* $\quad = \quad$ 1 vol $\quad + \quad \frac{13}{2}$ vol $\quad \rightarrow \quad$ 4 vol $\quad + \quad$ 5 vol

∴ *volumes* $\quad = \quad$ 20 cm^3 $\quad + \quad$ 130 cm^3 $\quad \rightarrow \quad$ 80 cm^3 $\quad + \quad$ 100 cm^3

∴ **Final composition** $\quad = \quad$ **80 cm^3 CO$_2$ + 100cm^3 H$_2$O**
Total volume $\qquad = \quad$ **180 cm^3**

● In other examples one of the reactants may be in **excess** or the water formed may not be a gas, depending on the **temperature**.

Example 17

What is the final composition and volume of the gas mixture produced when 100 cm^3 of ethene is sparked with 400 cm^3 of oxygen, if all measurements are made at 25 °C?

The chemical equation . . .

$$C_2H_4(g) \quad + \quad 3O_2(g) \quad \rightarrow \quad 2CO_2(g) \quad + \quad 2H_2O(l)$$

∴ *ratio* $\quad = \quad$ 1 vol $\quad + \quad$ 3 vol $\quad \rightarrow \quad$ 2 vol $\quad + \quad$ negligible*

∴ *volumes* $\quad = \quad$ 100 cm^3 $\quad + \quad$ 300 cm^3 $\quad \rightarrow \quad$ 200 cm^3 $\quad + \quad$ —

(100 cm^3 of O$_2$ is excess)

∴ **Final composition** $\quad = \quad$ **200 cm^3 CO$_2$ + 100 cm^3 O$_2$**
Total volume $\qquad = \quad$ **300 cm^3**

* In this example the water formed is a liquid, as the temperature is below 100 °C, so it has a negligible volume compared to the gases.

UNIT 2
THE WORLD OF CARBON

INTRODUCTION TO ORGANIC CHEMISTRY

The study of carbon containing compounds is called **organic chemistry**. This introduction to "The World of Carbon" considers the names, formulae and structures of the most common series of organic compounds.

At the end of this section you should be able to . . .   ✔

Describe the main features of organic compounds.   ❏

Explain the terms *functional group, homologous series* and *isomer*.   ❏

Write the name and structural formula, from C_1 to C_8, for . . .

            alkanes — alkenes — cycloalkanes — alkynes

            alkanols — alkanoic acids — alkanals — alkanones.   ❏

Use the systematic rules of nomenclature to name and draw branched and substituted compounds from the above groups.   ❏

Identify the following functional groups . . .

            hydroxyl — carboxyl — carbonyl — amino — C = C double bond —

            C ≡ C triple bond.   ❏

Explain the terms *alcohol, carboxylic acid, aldehyde* and *ketone*.   ❏

Explain the term *aromatic hydrocarbon* and give examples.   ❏

Draw and identify the benzene ring and phenyl group.   ❏

State names and formulae for simple substituted benzene compounds.   ❏

WORD LIST

The following words are introduced or used in this topic. You should be able to define, use and give examples of them where appropriate.

alcohol	amine	homologous series
aldehyde	amino group	hydrocarbon
alkanal	aromatic	hydroxyl group
alkane	benzene	isomer
alkanoic acid	carbonyl group	ketone
alkanol	carboxyl group	organic
alkanone	carboxylic acid	phenyl group
alkene	cycloalkane	
alkynes	functional group	

If you are not familiar with the meaning of any of these words, you should refer to the Glossary, where these words are defined.

FEATURES OF ORGANIC CHEMISTRY

The main features of organic chemistry are . . .

       millions of different compounds
          many examples of isomers
            homologous series
                and functional groups.

- There are **millions of organic compounds**, as carbon atoms can form chains and rings of different length and shape. Thus there are many more compounds of carbon than all the other elements put together.

- There are **many examples of isomers**, compounds with the same molecular formula but different structural formulae, as carbon atoms can bond in many different ways,

  e.g.   Butane has two isomers:

$$H - C - C - C - C - H \qquad \text{both} \qquad H - C - C - C - H$$

  both C_4H_{10}

  The larger the molecule the greater the number of possible isomers.

- Organic compounds usually fit into groups, called **homologous series**, with similar chemical properties, a general formula and showing a gradation in physical properties, e.g.

    Alkanes, alkenes, alkynes and cycloalkanes.

- Most organic compounds contain a **functional group**, a group of atoms which give the molecule characteristic properties,

  e.g.

  $$-O \diagup H \qquad\qquad \diagdown C = C \diagup$$

  hydroxyl   carbon-carbon
  group   double bond

  The functional group in a molecule can be used to identify the homologous series.

The most common **homologous series** and **functional groups** are shown on the next page along with an example.

The formula and structure of any member of these series (from C_1 to C_8) can be worked out by considering the functional group to be added to the corresponding alkane.

Homologous series	Functional group	Example
Alkane General formula C_nH_{2n+2}	none	 *Butane*
Alkene 2 less –H atoms than alkanes	C $=$ C double bond C $=$ C	 *Propene*
Alkyne 4 less –H atoms than alkanes	C $\equiv$ C triple bond — C $\equiv$ C —	H — C $\equiv$ C — H *Ethyne*
Cycloalkane 2 less –H atoms than alkanes	carbon ring	 *Cyclobutane*
* **Alcohols and alkanols** 1 more –O atom than alkanes	hydroxyl group — O	 *Propanol*
* **Aldehydes and Alkanals** 1 more –O and 2 less –H atoms than alkane	carbonyl group on end C atom — C	 *Butanal*
* **Ketones and Alkanones** 1 more –O and 2 less –H atoms than alkane	carbonyl group on a middle C atom O ‖ — C —	 *Propanone*
* **Carboxylic acids and Alkanoic acids** 2 more –O and 2 less –H atoms than alkane	carboxyl group — C O — H	 *Butanoic acid*

*   The names **alcohol**, **aldehydes**, **ketones** and **carboxylic acids** are used to describe any molecular structure which contains the **hydroxyl**, **carbonyl** or **carboxyl groups**.

*   The names **alkanol**, **alkanal**, **alkanone** and **alkanoic acid** are used to describe simple "straight chain" series of molecules which contain the **hydroxyl**, **carbonyl** or **carboxyl groups**.

NAMING ORGANIC COMPOUNDS

Organic compounds are named according to internationally accepted rules. The main rules for organic **nomenclature** are . . .

Rule 1   The **basic name** comes from the **longest continuous chain** of carbon atoms.

C_1	**meth** . . .		C_2	**eth** . . .
C_3	**prop** . . .		C_4	**but** . . .
C_5	**pent** . . .		C_6	**hex** . . .
C_7	**hept** . . .		C_8	**oct** . . .

Rule 2   The **name ending** comes from the **functional group**, which must be in the longest chain.

C — C single bonds . . .	$-\overset{\displaystyle\mid}{\underset{\displaystyle\mid}{C}}-$	. . . **ane**
C = C double bond . . .	C = C	. . . **ene**
C ≡ C triple bond . . .	—C ≡ C —	. . . **yne**
hydroxyl group . . .	$-\overset{\displaystyle\mid}{\underset{\displaystyle\mid}{C}}-O\diagup H$	. . . **anol**
carbonyl group (on end carbon) . . .	$-C\overset{\diagup\!\!O}{\diagdown H}$	. . . **anal**
carbonyl group (on middle carbon) . . .	$-\overset{\displaystyle\mid}{\underset{\displaystyle\mid}{C}}-\overset{\displaystyle O}{\overset{\displaystyle\|}{C}}-\overset{\displaystyle\mid}{\underset{\displaystyle\mid}{C}}-$	. . . **anone**
carboxyl group . . .	$-C\overset{\diagup\!\!O}{\diagdown O-H}$	. . . **anoic acid**

Rule 3   The position of the functional group is noted by **numbering each carbon atom** in the longest chain so that the functional group is given the lowest number possible.

Example 1

```
    H   H   H   H   H
    |   |   |   |   |
H — C — C — C — C — C — H
    |   |   |   |   |
    H   O   H   H   H
        \
         H
```

pentan-2-ol

Example 2

```
CH2 — CH = CH — CH3
|
CH2
|
CH3
```

Remember the longest chain is always counted.

hex-2-ene

Rule 4   Branches to the chain are named in alphabetical order and their position noted by numbering the chain as above.

CH_3- **methyl**
C_2H_5- **ethyl**
$Cl-$ **chloro**
$Br-$ **bromo**
NH_2- **amino**

Notice how the *amino group* is usually named like a branch, not a functional group.

Example 3   *Example 4*

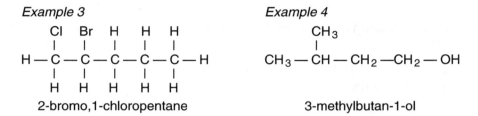

2-bromo,1-chloropentane   3-methylbutan-1-ol

Rule 5   Multiple groups and branches are noted by using a **prefix**.

Di . . .   2 of the same groups or branches
Tri . . .   3 of the same groups or branches
Tetra . . .   4 of the same groups or branches
etc.

Example 5   *Example 6*

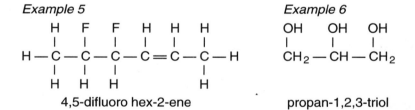

4,5-difluoro hex-2-ene   propan-1,2,3-triol

Naming Aromatic Hydrocarbons

Aromatic hydrocarbons are are based on the compound **benzene** which has a **ring structure** and a formula of C_6H_6.

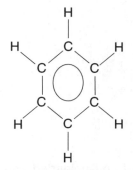

The structure of benzene is usually written in the shortened form as shown opposite.

Many aromatic compounds are formed by substituting one or more of the hydrogen atoms on the benzene molecule with another atom or group of atoms.

Substituted benzene compounds can be named in two ways.

With a prefix of the substituted group, e.g.

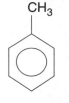

methyl benzene

chloro benzene

Or using the prefix **phenyl** to represent the **phenyl group $-C_6H_5$** shown below, e.g.

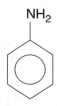

phenylamine
$C_6H_5NH_2$

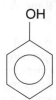

phenol
C_6H_5OH

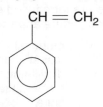

phenylethene
$C_6H_5C_2H_3$

FUELS

Reliable sources of **energy** are essential to modern industry and life. This section revises and extends earlier work on oil and **fuels**, including the chemistry and manufacture of petrol and use of alternative energy sources. The advantages and disadvantages of different fuels are also considered.

At the end of this section you should be able to . . .   ✔

Describe and explain *fractional distillation* and *catalytic cracking*.   ❐
State the names and uses of the main fractions from crude oil.   ❐
Explain the terms *fossil fuel* and *finite resource*.   ❐
Describe *reforming* and explain its purpose.   ❐
Describe the process of *blending* in petrol manufacture.   ❐
Describe how petrol is ignited in a car engine.   ❐
Describe and explain *auto-ignition* and *knocking* in petrol engines.   ❐
Explain the use of *lead additives* in petrol.   ❐
Explain the difference in molecular structure between leaded and unleaded petrol. ❐
Describe how ethanol can be formed from a *renewable* source.   ❐
Describe how ethanol can be used as an alternative fuel.   ❐
State some advantages and disadvantages of using methanol as an alternative to petrol. ❐
Explain the term *anaerobic fermentation*.   ❐
Describe the constituents of *biogas* and how it is produced.   ❐
Describe how methane can be used as a fuel.   ❐
Explain the term *the hydrogen economy*.   ❐
Describe the production and use of hydrogen for use as a fuel.   ❐
Describe ways in which the burning of fuels cause pollution problems.   ❐
Explain how the use of alternative fuels help protect the environment.   ❐
Explain the main advantages of using hydrogen instead of petrol.   ❐

WORD LIST

The following words are introduced or used in this topic. You should be able to define, use and give examples of them where appropriate.

acid rain	crude oil	gas oil	octane number
anaerobic	diesel	gasoline	oxygenates
auto-ignition	distillation	greenhouse effect	refining (oil)
biogas	fermentation	kerosine	reforming
biomass	finite	knocking	renewable source
bitumen	flammability	leaded petrol	thermal cracking
blended	fractional distillation	naphtha	unleaded petrol
combustion	fuel	natural gas	viscosity

If you are not familiar with the meaning of any of these words, you should refer to the Glossary, where these words are defined.

FOSSIL FUELS

A **fuel** is a substance which can be used as a **source of energy** and includes anything which will burn.

Fossil fuels like **coal**, **oil** and **natural gas** come from once living materials.

All fossil fuels are **finite resources**, as they will eventually run out. **Crude oil** and **natural gas** were **formed** over **millions of years** by the action of heat and pressure on the remains of **tiny sea creatures**.

The **crude oil** is a complex mixture of different **hydrocarbons**, varying in size from one carbon atom to over a hundred carbon atoms per molecule.

Hydrocarbons are made of **carbon** and **hydrogen** atoms only.

There are four main hydrocarbon series, **alkanes**, **alkenes**, **alkynes** and **cycloalkanes**, e.g.

$$H-\overset{\displaystyle \overset{H}{|}}{\underset{\displaystyle \underset{H}{|}}{C}}-H \qquad \overset{\displaystyle \overset{H \quad H}{| \quad |}}{\underset{\displaystyle \underset{H \quad H}{| \quad |}}{C=C}} \qquad H-C\equiv C-H$$

methane   **ethene**   **ethyne**   **cyclopropane**

Many of the **fuels** we use contain hydrocarbons which burn readily in air, forming the same products on **complete combustion**,

Hydrocarbon + Oxygen → Carbon dioxide + Water

e.g. $C_9H_{20} + 14O_2 \rightarrow 9CO_2 + 10H_2O$

OIL REFINING

Crude oil is the raw material for the **petrochemical industry**, which produces most of our **fuels** and a vast number of **consumer products**.

Oil refining involves three main processes, **fractional distillation**, **catalytic cracking** and **reforming**, which are used to separate and alter the constituents of the crude oil.

Fractional Distillation

The process of **fractional distillation** separates the components of a mixture into **fractions** depending on their boiling points.

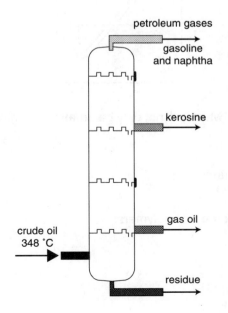

In industry the distillation of crude oil is carried out in a **fractionating tower** after the excess gases have been removed.

The oil is heated up until most of it has evaporated and turned into a gas.

The lower boiling point fractions are taken from the top of the tower while the higher boiling point fractions condense at the bottom of the tower.

A **fraction** is a group of molecules with boiling points within a given range.

This process can also be used to separate mixed products of other processes in the oil refinery. It is sometimes necessary to repeat the distillation to improve the separation.

Some typical fractions which can be produced by distillation are ...

fuel gases	$C_1 - C_4$	Increasing ...
gasoline (petrol)		**size of molecules,**
and naphtha	$C_5 - C_{10}$	**b.pt.** and **viscosity**
kerosene (paraffin)	$C_{10} - C_{14}$	
gas oil (diesel)	$C_{14} - C_{19}$	Decreasing ...
lubricating oils,		**flammability**
waxes and greases	$C_{19} - C_{70}$	
bitumen tar	over C_{70}	

Catalytic Cracking

Most crude oils contain higher proportions of the heavier fractions than are needed. Therefore, to meet the demand for the lighter fractions like gasoline and kerosine, the longer chain hydrocarbon molecules have to be broken up. This can be done by heating the heavy fractions, which literally shakes the long molecules, breaking them up into smaller bits. This process is called the **thermal cracking**.

In industry and in the laboratory, a **catalyst** of **aluminium oxide** is usually used. This is called **catalytic cracking** and it is more economical than thermal cracking as it allows the reaction to take place at a lower temperature.

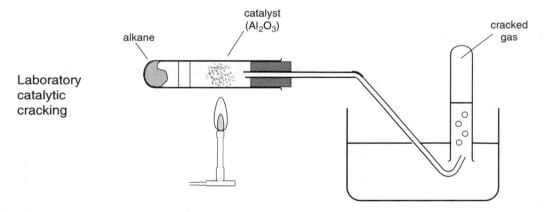

Laboratory catalytic cracking

Cracking will produce a variety of product molecules, which will not only be **smaller** but will also contain some **unsaturated hydrocarbon**,

$$\text{e.g.} \quad \underset{\text{Alkane}}{C_{20}H_{42}} \xrightarrow{\text{catalyst}} \underset{\text{Alkane}}{C_{12}H_{26}} + \underset{\text{Alkene}}{C_8H_{16}}$$

Catalytic cracking is the main industrial source of **alkenes** for polymers.

Reforming

Reforming describes a number of very important processes which use **catalysts** to alter the **arrangement of atoms** in molecules without necessarily changing the size of the molecules.

In **reforming**, hydrocarbons may be changed from . . .

> **straight chains to branched chains**
> **straight chains to cyclic structures**
> **cyclic structures to aromatic compounds.**

In **reforming**, the oil fraction is passed over a heated **catalyst of platinum**, causing the straight chain molecules to be rearranged into a variety of different products,

e.g. $C_6H_{14} \longrightarrow C_6H_{12} + H_2$
       hexane   cyclohexane   hydrogen

e.g. $C_6H_{12} \longrightarrow C_6H_6 + 3H_2$
   cyclohexane   benzene   hydrogen

PETROL AND PETROL ENGINES

In **petrol** engines, the fuel and air are mixed in the cylinder, compressed by the piston and the mixture **explodes** when it is ignited with a **spark**.

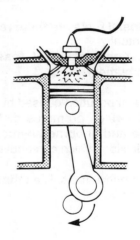

The engine is "timed" so that the fuel explodes as the piston reaches the top of the cylinder.

If the petrol ignites too soon, i.e. **auto-ignition**, the engine will run unevenly and could be damaged. This is called **"knocking"**.

BLENDING PETROL

The **gasoline fractions** (C_5 to C_{10}), which are used to make petrol, contain mainly straight chain molecules.
Straight chain molecules make a **low grade petrol**, which tends to cause **auto-ignition** and "knocking".

A **high grade petrol** can be produced in two ways.

● **Leaded petrol** uses the gasoline fraction from distillation, along with a **lead additive** to make it burn evenly.

● **Unleaded petrol** contains **reformed naphtha** fractions, which contain a high proportion of branched chain, cycloalkane and aromatic molecules, to make it burn evenly.

The **grade of a petrol** is measured by its **"octane number"**, the higher the number, the higher the grade and the more smoothly it burns.

To produce a specific grade of **petrol**, for use in particular conditions, different fractions and refinery products are **blended** together, e.g.

● more **volatile** components are added to the petrol blend in **colder** climates. This means adding more of the hydrocarbons with small molecules, like butane and pentane, so that the petrol vaporises more easily.

● the **octane number** can also be raised by adding more **reformed fractions** or **oxygenates**, which are compounds like alcohols, which contain carbon, hydrogen and oxygen.

Note   The use of **leaded petrol** is being reduced, as the lead is poisonous and also damages **catalytic converters** in car exhausts.

ALTERNATIVE FUELS

There are two reasons for research into **alternative fuel** sources.

● All **fossil fuels** are **finite resources**, so our reserves of coal, oil and natural gas will run out eventually.
● The **combustion** of **fossil fuels** causes problems of **pollution** and damages the environment.

The types of pollution caused by burning fossil fuels includes increasing levels of carbon dioxide in the air, which promotes global warming, incomplete combustion releasing soot, carbon monoxide and unburned hydrocarbons and side reactions which form nitrogen dioxide and sulphur dioxide, which contribute to acid rain.

Using alternative fuels, like **ethanol**, **methanol**, **methane**, or **hydrogen**, may relieve some or all of these problems.

ETHANOL

The **carbohydrates** in sugar cane and beet are **renewable** sources of **ethanol (C_2H_5OH)**, which can be used as a fuel.

Ethanol is made by the **fermentation** of **glucose** using the enzyme zymase in yeast, e.g.

$$C_6H_{12}O_6 \xrightarrow{\text{zymase}} 2C_2H_5OH + 2CO_2$$
$$\text{Glucose} \qquad\qquad \text{Ethanol}$$

In some countries, ethanol is used as an additive to petrol, or even in place of petrol, as the fuel for car engines.

The complete combustion of ethanol produces carbon dioxide and water only.

$$C_2H_5OH + 3O_2 \longrightarrow 2CO_2 + 3H_2O$$

The main **advantages** of using **ethanol** are . . .

● ethanol comes from a renewable plant source (sugar cane) and any carbon dioxide released on combustion will be removed by the photosynthesis reactions which occur in reforming the carbohydrate.

● ethanol is a cleaner fuel than petrol or diesel, as it tends to burn completely, producing carbon dioxide and water only.

METHANOL

Methanol is made by passing **synthesis gas**, a mixture of **carbon monoxide** and **hydrogen**, over a heated catalyst.

$$CO \ + \ 2H_2 \longrightarrow CH_3OH$$
synthesis gas   **methanol**

There are **advantages** and **disadvantages** in using methanol as a fuel instead of petrol.

● *Advantages* Methanol is a clean fuel, it burns more completely and produces less carbon monoxide.
Methanol fuels contain no aromatic hydrocarbons which are carcinogenic (cancer causing).

● *Disadvantages* Methanol is highly toxic and could be dangerous.
Methanol absorbs water from the air and is more likely to cause engine corrosion than petrol.

METHANE — BIOGAS

In the absence of oxygen, certain bacteria can act on **biomass**, organic material like compost or sewage, to produce a **fuel gas**.
This process is called **anaerobic** (without air) **fermentation** and the fuel gas is called **biogas**.

Biogas is mainly **methane** and burns like other hydrocarbons.

$$CH_4 \ + \ 2O_2 \longrightarrow CO_2 \ + \ 2H_2O$$

Although not widely used at present, **biogas** could be an economic fuel in rural areas where the compost and manure would be a **renewable source** of the fuel and in constant supply.

HYDROGEN

Hydrogen can be burned in an **engine** or used to produce electricity in a hydrogen-oxygen **fuel cell**. Hydrogen is an excellent source of different forms of **energy**.

Hydrogen is the only **pollution free** fuel, as the combustion of hydrogen only produces water,

i.e. $$2H_2 + O_2 \longrightarrow 2H_2O$$

Therefore there is no increase in the level of carbon dioxide or other products from incomplete combustion.

Hydrogen can be produced by the **electrolysis of water**. If the electricity used in the cell is produced from solar energy and not fossil fuels, the hydrogen can be regarded as a **renewable source** of energy.

At present the production of hydrogen is too expensive to make a **"hydrogen economy"** cost-effective. However, research continues and the future could see hydrogen gas being used as the main means of storing and distributing energy.

ORGANIC CHEMICAL REACTIONS

This section introduces the main **chemical reactions** involving alkenes, alkynes, aromatics, alcohols and esters. It also deals with the calculation of percentage yields in chemical reactions.

At the end of this section you should be able to . . .   ✔

Explain the terms *saturated* and *unsaturated hydrocarbon*.   ❐
Name and draw the products formed when halogens, hydrogen or hydrogen halides
    are added to alkenes.   ❐
Name and draw the products formed when water is *added* to alkenes.   ❐
Explain the terms *hydration* and *hydrogenation*.   ❐
Name and draw the products formed when halogens, hydrogen or hydrogen halides
    are added to alkynes.   ❐
Describe how alcohols can be converted to alkenes.   ❐
Name and draw the products of the dehydration of an alcohol.   ❐
Describe the structure of the benzene molecule and related compounds.   ❐
Explain the reaction between benzene and bromine water and the stability of the
    benzene ring.   ❐
Identify alcohols as *primary*, *secondary* or *tertiary*.   ❐
Name and draw the products of *oxidising* alcohols.   ❐
Name an oxidising agent which can be used to oxidise an alcohol.   ❐
Name and draw the products of oxidising an aldehyde.   ❐
Describe the action of different oxidising agents on different organic series (ppa).   ❐
Describe and explain a simple test to tell aldehydes from ketones.   ❐
Describe oxidation and reduction in terms of the oxygen/hydrogen ratio of the molecules.   ❐
Explain the terms *ester*, *condensation* and *hydrolysis reactions*.   ❐
Draw and identify the ester link and explain how it is formed.   ❐
Describe how an ester can be formed in the laboratory (ppa).   ❐
Name and draw the structure of an ester formed from given reactants.   ❐
Describe how esters can be broken up and name the type of reaction.   ❐
Name and draw the structures of the products formed by breaking up an ester.   ❐
Calculate the percentage yield of product from given data.   ❐

WORD LIST

The following words are introduced or used in this topic. You should be able to define, use and give examples of them where appropriate.

addition reaction	hydration	saturated hydrocarbon
Benedict's solution	hydrogenation	secondary alcohol
condensation reaction	hydrolysis reaction	tertiary alcohol
dehydration	oxidation (organic)	unsaturated hydrocarbon
ester	primary alcohol	
esterification	reduction (organic)	

If you are not familiar with the meaning of any of these words, you should refer to the Glossary, where these words are defined.

ADDITION REACTIONS OF ALKENES

The **alkenes** like ethene, propene and butene are called **unsaturated hydrocarbons** as they contain a $C = C$ **double bond** and undergo **addition reactions**,
e.g.

```
 H   H                                              H   H   H
 |   |                                              |   |   |
 C = C                                          H — C — C = C
 |   |                                              |       |
 H   H                                              H       H
```
ethene   **propene**
C_2H_4 C_3H_6

In **addition reactions**, the attacking molecule **breaks the double bond** and **"adds on"** to the two carbon atoms on either side.

Diatomic molecules like **halogens**, **hydrogen halides** and **hydrogen gas** can take part in addition reaction with alkenes,

e.g.

```
                                                    H   H
                                                    |   |
           ┌────────── +    Br₂    ──────→      H — C — C — H
           │                                        |   |
           │                                        Br  Br
           │                                   1,2 dibromoethane
           │
 H   H     │                                        H   H
 |   |     │                                         |   |
 C = C     │          +    HBr    ──────→      H — C — C — H
 |   |     │                                        |   |
 H   H     │                                        H   Br
ethene     │                                    bromoethane
           │
           │                                        H   H
           │                                        |   |
           └────────── +    *H₂   ──────→      H — C — C — H
                               catalyst             |   |
                                  Ni                H   H
                                                   ethane
```

During the **addition reaction**, the $C = C$ **double bond** is removed and a $C - C$ **single bond** is formed. The addition reaction changes the **unsaturated** hydrocarbon into a **saturated** molecule.

* **Note**   The addition of hydrogen to an alkene is called **hydrogenation**.

HYDRATION OF ALKENES

Ethanol can be made by the fermentation of glucose but, to meet market demands, most ethanol is now manufactured by a process called the **catalytic hydration** of **ethene**.
This involves adding water to ethene in the presence of a catalyst, e.g.

$$C_2H_4 \quad + \quad H_2O \quad \longrightarrow \quad C_2H_5OH$$

Other **alcohols** can be made by the **hydration** of an appropriate **alkene**. (Only methanol cannot be made this way, as there is no suitable alkene.)

DEHYDRATION OF AN ALCOHOL

The reverse reaction, to change an **alcohol** into an **alkene**, called the **dehydration of an alcohol**, can be carried out in industry and the laboratory by using a **catalyst of aluminium oxide**.

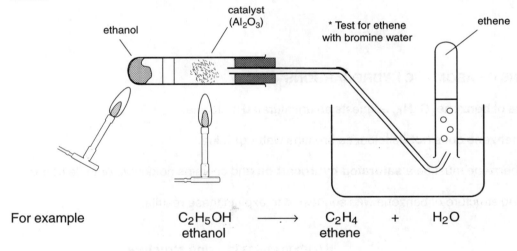

For example

$$\underset{\text{ethanol}}{C_2H_5OH} \quad \longrightarrow \quad \underset{\text{ethene}}{C_2H_4} \quad + \quad H_2O$$

ADDITION REACTIONS OF ALKYNES

Alkynes are a series of hydrocarbons which contain **one $C \equiv C$ triple bond**,

e.g.

$$H - C \equiv C - H$$

ethyne
C_2H_2

propyne
C_3H_4

The **alkynes** are another example of an **unsaturated hydrocarbon** series as they take part in **addition reactions** with **halogens**, **hydrogen halides** and **hydrogen gas** to form saturated molecules.

The alkynes undergo addition reactions, in two stages,

e.g.

$$H-C\equiv C-H \ + \ Br_2 \ \rightarrow \ \underset{\underset{\displaystyle Br \quad Br}{|\qquad|}}{\overset{\overset{\displaystyle H \quad H}{|\qquad|}}{C=C}} \ + \ Br_2 \ \rightarrow \ \underset{\underset{\displaystyle Br \quad Br}{|\qquad|}}{\overset{\overset{\displaystyle Br \quad Br}{|\qquad|}}{H-C-C-H}}$$

Ethyne	1,2-dibromoethene	1,1,2,2,-tetra-bromoethane

Bromine Water Test

The speed of decolourising **bromine water** can be used as a **test** to differentiate between **saturated** and **unsaturated** hydrocarbons.

● **Unsaturated hydrocarbons** like alkenes and alkynes decolourise bromine water **quickly** due to the fast addition reaction.

● **Saturated hydrocarbons** like alkanes and cycloalkanes decolourise bromine water **slowly**.

REACTIONS OF AROMATIC HYDROCARBONS

The formula of **benzene, C_6H_6**, suggests an unsaturated molecule.

However, **benzene** does **not** decolourise bromine water **quickly**.

Therefore benzene must be a **saturated hydrocarbon** and contains no double or triple bonds.

The following structure of benzene was suggested to explain these results,

i.e.

6 carbon atoms in a **ring structure**.

No double bonds but **6 delocalised electrons** around the ring and not attached to any particular carbon atom.

This is a **saturated** structure.

The benzene ring is very stable due to the delocalised electrons

Benzene can take part in some reactions where one or more of the hydrogen atoms are replaced by another atom or group of atoms.

Benzene does **not** undergo addition reactions as there are **no** double bonds.

OXIDATION REACTIONS

In organic chemistry, **oxidation reactions** often involve the addition of oxygen to a compound.

Combustion is the complete oxidation of a compound,

e.g.   Alcohols burn $C_4H_9OH + 6O_2 \longrightarrow 4CO_2 + 5H_2O$
            in oxygen   butanol

The **partial oxidation** of certain organic series, such as alcohols, is a useful route to the manufacture of many different organic compounds.

TYPES OF ALCOHOL

The hydration of alkenes can lead to the formation of **three** different **types** of **alcohol** depending on the position of the −OH group,

e.g.

```
    H   H   H                    H   H   H                    H   CH3 H
    |   |   |                    |   |   |                    |   |   |
H — C — C — C — H        H — C — C — C — H        H — C — C — C — H
    |   |   |                    |   |   |                    |   |   |
    H   H   O                    H   O   H                    H   O   H
             \                        \                            \
              H                        H                            H
```

   propan-1-ol   **propan-2-ol**   **2-methylpropan-2-ol**

This is a . . .   This is a . . .   This is a . . .
primary alcohol.   **secondary alcohol.**   **tertiary alcohol.**
The — OH is bonded to   The — OH is bonded to   The — OH is bonded to
a C with 2 — H atoms   a C with 1 — H atom   a C with no — H atoms

The different types of alcohol have different chemical properties and uses. In particular, the products formed by certain oxidation reactions depend on the type of alcohol involved.

OXIDATION OF ALCOHOLS

The **partial oxidation** of an alcohol can be brought about by a suitable **oxidising agent**, e.g.
                    acidified potassium dichromate solution,
                    acidified potassium permanganate solution,
                    heated solid copper(II)oxide.

The oxidation of different alcohols can yield a variety of products.

EQUATIONS FOR OXIDATION REACTION

Organic **oxidation** reactions involve either the **addition of oxygen** or the **removal of hydrogen** from a molecule, i.e.

> ● **Oxidation increases** the **oxygen to hydrogen** ratio of the molecule.

Primary alcohols form two products in a **two step oxidation**.

Step 1

2 — H atoms removed

propan-1-ol + oxidising → **propanal** + water
                   agent

Step 2

— O added to form — OH

propanal + oxidising → **propanoic acid**
               agent

Secondary alcohols can form only **one product** on oxidation.

As before 2 — H atoms removed

propan-2-ol + oxidising → **propanone** + water
                  agent

The general equations for oxidation are . . .

primary alcohol	+	**[O]**	→	**alkanal (aldehyde)**
alkanal (aldehyde)	+	**[O]**	→	**alkanoic acid**
secondary alcohol	+	**[O]**	→	**alkanone (ketone)**

Note that **reduction** is the **opposite** reaction to **oxidation** and involves either the **removal of oxygen** or the **addition of hydrogen** from a molecule, i.e.

> ● **Reduction decreases** the **oxygen to hydrogen** ratio of the molecule.

ALDEHYDES, KETONES AND CARBOXYLIC ACIDS

Aldehydes, **ketones** and **carboxylic acids** are all series of compounds which can be formed by the oxidation of an appropriate alcohol.

Aldehydes are formed by the 'one step' oxidation of **primary alcohols**.

Aldehydes have a **carbonyl group** on the end of a carbon chain,

e.g. propanal

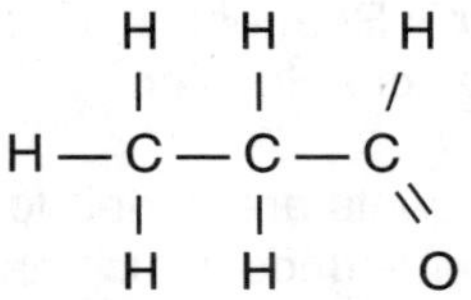

```
      H   H    H
      |   |   /
  H — C — C — C
      |   |    \\
      H   H    O
```

Alkanals are the straight chain series of **aldehydes**.

Ketones are formed by the oxidation of **secondary alcohols**.

Ketones have a carbonyl group linked to two other carbon atoms in the middle of a carbon chain,

e.g. butanone

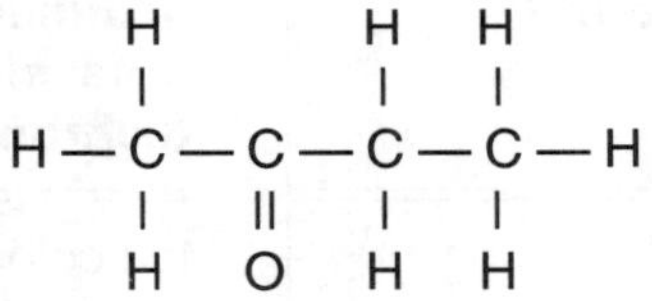

```
      H       H   H
      |       |   |
  H — C — C — C — C — H
      |   ||  |   |
      H   O   H   H
```

Alkanones are the straight chain series of **ketones**.

Carboxylic acids are formed by the 'two step' oxidation of **primary alcohols**.

Carboxylic acids contain the **carboxyl group** on the end of a carbon chain,

e.g. propanoic acid

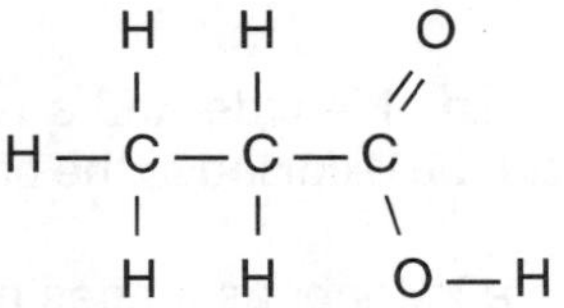

```
      H   H    O
      |   |   //
  H — C — C — C
      |   |    \
      H   H    O — H
```

Alkanoic acids are the straight chain series of **carboxylic acids.**

Note   **Ethanoic acid** can be produced by **bacterial oxidation** of ethanol. This is how wine, cider, etc., can turn into **vinegar** (a solution of ethanoic acid) when exposed to air.

Investigating organic oxidation reactions

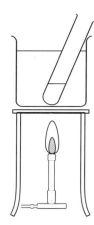

Aim

To use different mild oxidising agents to distinguish between two given carbonyl compounds, labelled **"X"** and **"Y"**, one an aldehyde and the other a ketone.

Method

The three mild oxidising agents used are . . .
- acidified potassium dichromate
- Tollen's Reagent
- Benedict's Solution.

The oxidising agents are added to test-tubes of the carbonyl compounds, which are then placed in a water bath for a few minutes. Care is required as the carbonyl compounds are **flammable** and the oxidising agents **harmful**.

Results

Carbonyl compound	Effect on acidified potassium dichromate	Effect on Tollen's Reagent	Effect on Benedict's Solution
X	the colour changes from orange to green	a silver mirror forms on the test-tube	the colour changes from blue to orange
Y	no change occurs	no change occurs	no change occurs

Conclusions

"X" must be an aldehyde and a reducing agent, as it reacts with all the oxidising agents and aldehydes can be oxidised to the corresponding carboxylic acid.

"Y" must be a ketone, as it does not react with the oxidising agents and ketones are not easily oxidised.

ESTERS

Esters are a series of organic compounds formed by a **condensation reaction** between an **alcohol** and a **carboxylic acid**.

During this **condensation reaction**, a water molecule is eliminated by removing **— H** from the alcohol and **— OH** from the carboxylic acid, e.g.

$$CH_3 - C \overset{O}{\underset{O-H}{\diagdown\diagup}} \quad + \quad H - O - CH_2 - CH_3 \rightleftharpoons CH_3 - C \overset{O}{\underset{O-CH_2-CH_3}{\diagup\diagdown}} \quad + \quad H_2O$$

ethanoic acid   +   ethanol $\rightleftharpoons$ ethyl ethanoate   +   water

$\rightleftharpoons$ Esterification, the reaction forming the ester, is reversible.

NAMING ESTERS

The **name** of the ester comes from the **alcohol** and **carboxylic acid**,

e.g.   Methanol and Propanoic acid $\longrightarrow$ Methyl propanoate
       Propanol and Methanoic acid $\longrightarrow$ Propyl methanoate
       Butanol and Ethanoic acid $\longrightarrow$ Butyl ethanoate
       etc.

THE STRUCTURE OF ESTERS

The **esters** linking group is . . .

from the acid $-C \overset{O}{\underset{O-C}{\diagup\diagdown}}$ from the alkanol

. . . formed by eliminating water from the hydroxyl group on the alcohol and the carboxyl group on the carboxylic acid.

By recognising this linking group and noting the position of the $= O$, we can name esters from their structural formulae.

Examples of simple esters are . . .

Example 1

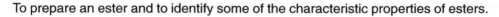

methyl propanoate

from acid

from alkanol

Example 2 $CH_3CH_2OOCCH_2CH_2CH_3$ **ethyl butanoate**

from   from
alkanol   acid

Preparation of Simple Esters

Aim

To prepare an ester and to identify some of the characteristic properties of esters.

Method

To prepare an ester, the alcohol and carboxylic acid are warmed gently in the presence of a few drops of concentrated sulphuric acid, which acts as a catalyst.

A water bath is used as both reactants and products are flammable.

After a few minutes, the contents of the test-tube are "tipped" into sodium carbonate solution to neutralise the excess acid.

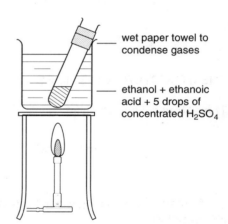

wet paper towel to condense gases

ethanol + ethanoic acid + 5 drops of concentrated H_2SO_4

Results

The ester can be recognised by its distinctive **smell** and the fact that it is **insoluble** in water and forms a separate layer on top of the water.

BREAKING UP ESTERS

The **break-up** of an **ester** can be brought about by warming the ester with an **alkali** like sodium hydroxide solution.

This is a **hydrolysis reaction** as a water molecule is added to break up the structure and produce the alcohol and carboxylic acid, e.g.

$$
\begin{array}{ccc}
H & H & O \\
| & | & \| \\
H-C-C-C & & H \\
| & | & \backslash \quad | \\
H & H & O-C-H \\
& & | \\
& & H
\end{array}
\qquad + \qquad H_2O
$$

methyl propanoate   water

$$
\begin{array}{ccc}
H & H & O \\
| & | & /\!/ \\
H-C-C-C & & \\
| & | & \backslash \\
H & H & O-H
\end{array}
\quad + \quad
\begin{array}{cc}
H & H \\
\backslash & | \\
O-C-H \\
& | \\
& H
\end{array}
$$

propanoic acid   methanol

The break up of an ester is also a reversible reaction.

As the formation and break-up of esters are reversible reactions, an equilibrium will exist . . .

$$
\boxed{\;\text{ACID} \;+\; \text{ALKANOL} \;\underset{\text{hydrolysis}}{\overset{\text{condensation}}{\rightleftharpoons}}\; \text{ESTER} \;+\; \text{WATER}\;}
$$

PERCENTAGE YIELDS

The **percentage yield** of products in a reaction can be calculated by comparing the **actual yield** obtained with the calculated **theoretical yield**.

$$\textbf{Percentage yield} \ = \ \frac{\textbf{actual yield}}{\textbf{theoretical yield}} \ \times \ \textbf{100}$$

Example

When 5·2 g of ethanol is mixed with excess ethanoic acid and a few drops of concentrated sulphuric acid, 8·12 g of ethyl ethanoate are formed. What is the percentage yield of ethyl ethanoate?

*The **balanced chemical equation** is needed to calculate the theoretical yield.*

$$C_2H_5OH \ + \ CH_3COOH \longrightarrow CH_3COOC_2H_5 \ + \ H_2O$$

This gives us the mole ratio

∴   1 mole of ethanol   ⇔   1 mole of ethyl ethanoate

Now calculate the mass of one mole of the reactants and products

1 mole of C_2H_5OH 1 mole of $CH_3COOC_2H_5$
    $= (2 \times 12) + (5 \times 1) + 16 + 1$ $= 12 + (3 \times 1) + 12 + 16$
    $= 46$ g $+ 16 + (2 \times 12) + (5 \times 1)$
                                                       $= 88$ g

Substitute in the mole ratio and calculate the theoretical yield

∴   46 g of ethanol   ⇔   88 g of ethyl ethanoate

∴   1 g of ethanol   ⇔ $\dfrac{88}{46}$ g

∴   5·2 g of ethanol   ⇔ $5{\cdot}2 \times \dfrac{88}{46}$

                            =   9·95 g of ethyl ethanoate

∴   Percentage yield $= \dfrac{\text{actual yield}}{\text{theoretical yield}} \times 100$

                            $= \dfrac{8{\cdot}12}{9{\cdot}95} \times 100$

                            =   **81.6 % yield of ethyl ethanoate**

USES OF ORGANIC COMPOUNDS

This short section introduces some of the **uses** of different **organic compounds**. It also considers the competing demands between the use of petrochemicals for fuels or for feedstocks for the chemical industry.

At the end of this section you should be able to ...   ✔

Explain the competing demands for the use of crude oil products.   ❏
Recognise that many consumer products are made from carbon containing compounds.   ❏
State some uses of alcohols.   ❏
State some uses of carboxylic acids.   ❏
State some uses of esters.   ❏
Describe how aromatic compounds can be made from benzene.   ❏
Name and draw the structure of some examples of consumer products made from
aromatic compounds.   ❏
Describe the main properties and uses of haloalkanes.   ❏
Explain some problems associated with the use of haloalkanes.   ❏

WORD LIST

The following words are introduced or used in this topic. You should be able to define, use and give examples of them where appropriate.

chlorofluorocarbon   haloalkanes
feedstock   Halogen

If you are not familiar with the meaning of any of these words, you should refer to the Glossary, where these words are defined.

USES OF PETROCHEMICALS

There are competing demands between using our resources of **crude oil** for **fuels** and for **feedstocks** for the manufacture of **consumer products**.
Many consumer products like plastics, textiles, cosmetics, detergents, dyes, agrochemicals and pharmaceuticals are made from **compounds of carbon**, e.g.

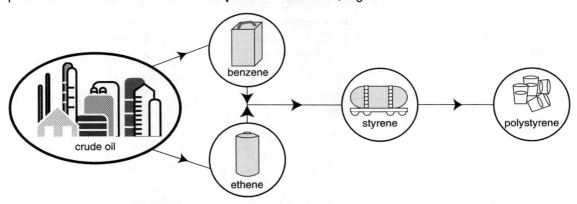

It may be easier to find alternative sources of energy than new sources of feedstocks for the chemical industry.

USES OF ALCOHOLS AND CARBOXYLIC ACIDS

Oxidation of alcohols makes **aldehydes**, **ketones** and **carboxylic acids**.
Alcohols are used as **solvents** for extracting oils and in varnishes.
Ethanol is the alcohol in **alcoholic drinks**.
Alcohols and carboxylic acids are used for making **esters** and **polyesters**.
Ethanoic acid is found in **vinegar** and used to make **polymers** like PVA.
Stearic acid and oleic acid are used to make soap.

USES OF ESTERS

Esters are used as **food flavourings**, e.g. pentyl ethanoate — banana.
Esters are sweet smelling and used in **perfumes**.
Ethyl ethanoate is used as a **solvent** in adhesives and nail varnish.

USES OF AROMATIC COMPOUNDS

Benzene and its related **aromatic compounds** are important feedstocks in the chemical industry, being used to make a large number of products, including medicines, paints, artificial fibres, dyes and explosives.
Benzene is made by **reforming** the **naphtha** fraction from crude oil.
Many different **feedstocks** and **consumer products** can be made by **substituting** one or more of the hydrogen atoms on the benzene molecule.

Examples

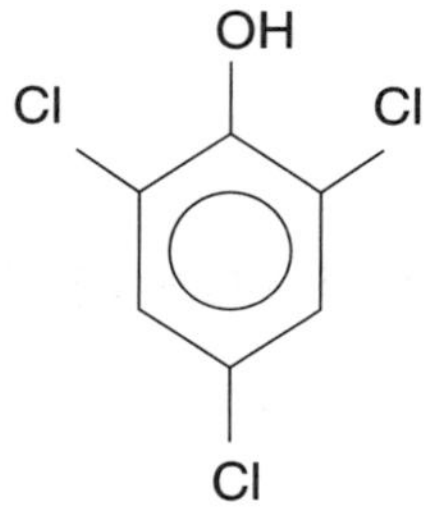

trichlorophenol
(T.C.P.) used as
an antiseptic

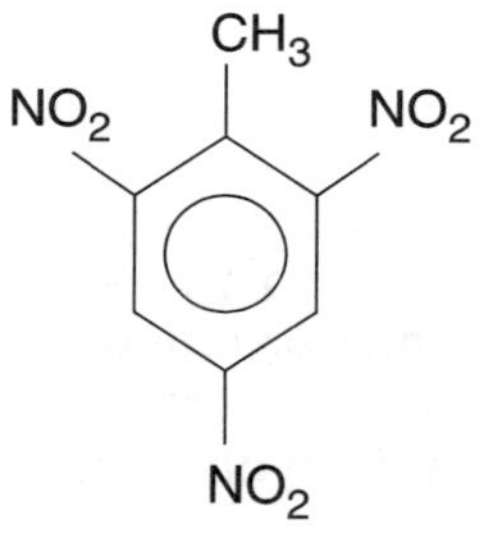

trinitrotoluene
(T.N.T) used as
an explosive

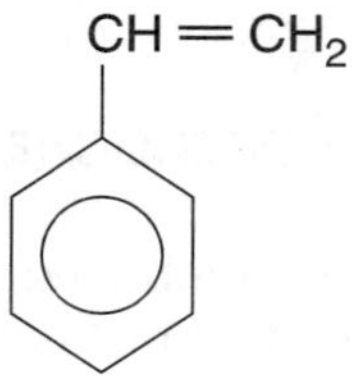

phenylethene
(styrene) used to
make polystyrene

USES OF HALOALKANES

Haloalkanes are alkane molecules with one or more hydrogen atoms substituted by halogens.

The **haloalkanes** are useful as they tend to be **less reactive**, **flammable** and **toxic** than many other organic compounds.

Example

$$Cl - \underset{\underset{\displaystyle Cl}{|}}{\overset{\overset{\displaystyle Cl}{|}}{C}} - \underset{\underset{\displaystyle H}{|}}{\overset{\overset{\displaystyle H}{|}}{C}} - H$$

1,1,1-trichloroethane
used as a solvent

The commonest group of haloalkanes are the **chlorofluorocarbons (CFCs)** which are used as . . .

refrigerants in cooling systems,
solvents for dry cleaning,
propellants in sprays.

Example

$$Cl - \underset{\underset{\displaystyle Cl}{|}}{\overset{\overset{\displaystyle Cl}{|}}{C}} - F$$

Trichlorofluoromethane used as a refrigerant.

Disadvantages of using CFCs

The main disadvantage of using **CFCs** is the problems they cause in the **upper atmosphere**, where they **reduce** the **ozone (O_3)** concentrations, i.e.

In the upper atmosphere CFCs are broken down by sunlight

$$CCl_3F \rightarrow CCl_2F + Cl$$

and the chlorine atoms released react with ozone molecules

$$Cl + O_3 \rightarrow ClO + O_2$$

The "ozone layer" in the atmosphere is important as it absorbs harmful **ultra-violet radiation** and a reduction in ozone can cause a number of health problems, including increased risk of **skin cancer**.

It has now been agreed to phase out the use of CFCs over the next few years and they will be replaced by **hydrofluorocarbons (HFCs)** which are similar but less stable so they break down in the lower atmosphere without affecting the "ozone layer".

POLYMERS

Plastics and **synthetic fibres**, which are called **polymers**, are amongst the most important new materials devised by man. This section looks at the manufacture and properties of a range of different polymers, both old and new.

At the end of this section you should be able to . . .   ✔

Explain the importance of ethene to the petrochemical industry.   ❏
Describe two ways of producing ethene and propene in industry.   ❏
Explain how *addition polymers*, like polyethene, are formed.   ❏
Give names, structures and uses of some *addition polymers*.   ❏
Draw the repeating unit and polymer structure of an addition polymer given the monomer
          structure and vice versa.   ❏
Explain the difference between *high and low density* poly(ethene).   ❏
Explain the difference between *isotactic and atactic* poly(propene).   ❏
Explain how *condensation polymers* are formed.   ❏
Identify monomers suitable for condensation polymerisation.   ❏
Draw the repeating unit and polymer structure of a condensation polymer given the
          structures of the monomers and vice versa.   ❏
Describe with examples how *polyesters* are formed.   ❏
Explain the difference between polyester *resins* and polyester *fibres*.   ❏
Identify and draw an *amine* and the *amino group*.   ❏
Explain how a *polyamide* and an *amide link* is formed.   ❏
Describe and explain the properties and uses of nylon.   ❏
Describe two ways to form *synthesis gas*.   ❏
Explain how methanal is formed from synthesis gas.   ❏
Describe how methanal is used to make a *thermosetting plastic*.   ❏
Explain the properties of *thermosetting* and *thermosoftening* plastics.   ❏
Describe the structure, properties and uses of Kevlar.   ❏
Describe the production, structure, properties and uses of poly(ethanol).   ❏
Describe the bonding, structure, properties and uses of poly(ethyne).   ❏
Describe the properties and uses of poly(vinyl carbozole).   ❏
Describe the manufacture, properties and uses of biopol and photodegradable low
          density polythene.   ❏

WORD LIST

The following words are introduced or used in this topic. You should be able to define, use and give examples of them where appropriate.

addition polymer	monomer	polyethyne
amide link	nylon	Polymer
atactic polymer	Photoconducting	polypeptide
biodegradable	photodegradable polymers	polypropene
Biopol	polyamide	poly vinyl carbazol
condensation polymer	polyester	synthesis gas
cross-link	polyester fibre	thermosetting polymer
isotactic polymer	polyester resin	thermosoftening polymer
Kevlar	polyethanol	
lattice structure	polyethene	

If you are not familiar with the meaning of any of these words, you should refer to the Glossary, where these words are defined.

EARLY PLASTICS AND SYNTHETIC FIBRES

Among the first plastics and synthetic fibres to be made commercially were **phenol-methanal** or bakelite (1910), **poly(ethene)** (1939) and **nylon** (1940). A range of many different plastics and synthetic fibres are now widely available and used in place of natural materials as they have many useful properties.

Polymers can be split into **two classes** depending on the way they are affected by heat.

● Some plastics **soften on heating**, so they are easily moulded into shape after they are formed,

e.g. polyethene and nylon

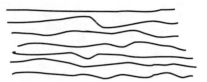

These are called **thermoplastic plastics**. They have long single chain molecules.

● Some plastics **do not soften on heating** but set hard when they are formed. These plastics are useful for places where they may meet high temperatures, e.g. kitchen worktops and the handles of pots and kettles,

e.g. bakelite and melamine

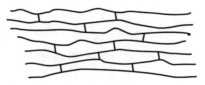

These are called **thermosetting plastics**. They have long molecules with cross-links.

ADDITION POLYMERS

Addition polymers are polymers made from **monomers** which contain a $C = C$ **double bond**. During **addition polymerisation**, the $C = C$ **double bond** opens up to allow the monomer units to join together.

Most of the monomers suitable for addition polymerisation are **petrochemicals** formed from crude oil fractions.

The alkenes **ethene** and **propene** are two important feedstocks in the petrochemical industry which can also be used to make addition polymers.

Ethene and **propene** can be produced from two main sources in industry.

● The **cracking** of the **naphtha** fraction from crude oil produces a variety of smaller hydrocarbon molecules, including **ethene**, **propene** and other unsaturated molecules,

e.g. $$C_9H_{20} \rightarrow C_4H_{10} + C_2H_4 + C_3H_6$$

● The **cracking of ethane or propane** from the gas fraction will produce **ethene** and **propene** respectively,

i.e. $$C_2H_6 \rightarrow C_2H_4 + H_2$$
$$C_3H_8 \rightarrow C_3H_6 + H_2$$

Ethene is the simplest **monomer** suitable for **addition polymerisation** . . .

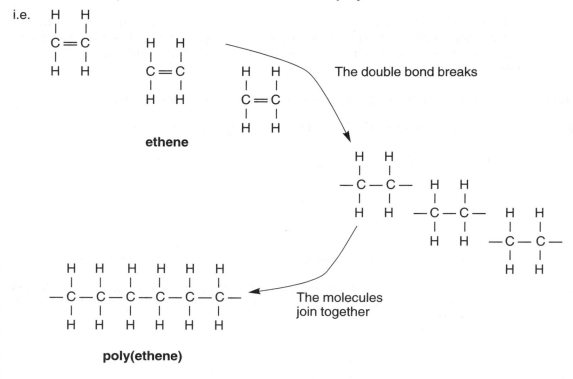

i.e.

ethene

The double bond breaks

The molecules
join together

poly(ethene)

Poly(propene) is also a very important addition polymer, used to make fibres for carpets, ropes and clothing.

propene   poly(propene)

STRUCTURE AND PROPERTIES

The molecules in **addition polymers** will contain **thousands of monomer units** linked together. These **long polymer chains** will not be perfectly linear but will "zig-zag" and may have **side branches**. Changes to the structure of a polymer can result in changes in properties.

The **number** and **size** of **side chains** can affect the properties of polymers like poly(ethene).

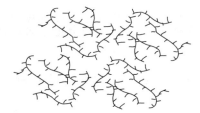

Low density poly(ethene)
(LDPE) Highly branched polymer, so
chains cannot pack closely together.

High density poly(ethene)
(HDPE) Few branches on polymer, so
chains can pack closely together.

The **arrangement** of the **side chains** can also affect the properties.

Atactic poly(propene) has the methyl branches randomly placed on either side of the carbon chain.

Isotactic poly(propene) has all the methyl branches on the same side of the carbon chain.

Isotactic polymers are stronger as the **chains** pack **closer** together.

CONDENSATION POLYMERS

Condensation polymers are formed by **eliminating** a small molecule, like water, from **monomers** which have **two functional groups** per molecule.

The monomers for condensation polymerisation will often contain the groups shown below . . .

$$
-\!\!C\!\!\underset{\displaystyle \diagdown}{\overset{\displaystyle O}{\diagup\diagup}} \qquad
-\!\!C\!\!\underset{\displaystyle O-H}{\overset{\displaystyle O}{\diagup\diagup}} \qquad
-\!\!N\!\!\underset{\displaystyle H}{\overset{\displaystyle H}{\diagup}} \qquad
-\!\!C-O
$$

POLYESTERS

Polyesters are **condensation polymers** formed by reacting **diols**, alcohols with two $-OH$ groups, with **diacids**, carboxylic acids with two $-COOH$ groups,

i.e.

$$
HO-\overset{\displaystyle O}{\overset{\displaystyle \|}{C}}-\square-\overset{\displaystyle O}{\overset{\displaystyle \|}{C}}-OH \quad \text{and} \quad HO-\blacksquare-OH
$$

                diacid   **diol**

Where $\square$ and $\blacksquare$ represent different arrangements of carbon and hydrogen atoms

e.g. a polyester called **terylene** is made from the following monomers.

$$
HO-CH_2-CH_2-OH \quad + \quad HOOC-\langle O \rangle-COOH
$$

        ethan-1,2-diol   benzene-1,4-dicarboxylic acid

The polymer chains are formed by a **condensation reaction** which eliminates water . . .

$$
-\!\!-CH_2-CH_2-O-\overset{\displaystyle O}{\overset{\displaystyle \|}{C}}-\langle O \rangle-\overset{\displaystyle O}{\overset{\displaystyle \|}{C}}-O-CH_2-CH_2-O-\overset{\displaystyle O}{\overset{\displaystyle \|}{C}}-\langle O \rangle-\overset{\displaystyle O}{\overset{\displaystyle \|}{C}}-\!\!- \quad + \quad 3H_2O
$$

terylene

There are two main types of polyester . . .

Textile **polyester fibres** which have **long chain** polymer molecules

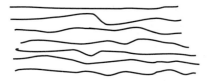

Producing a strong, flexible structure which can be used for making fabrics.

Cured **polyester resins** which have 3-dimensional structure with **cross-links** between the chains

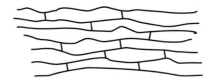

Producing a strong, rigid structure which is suitable for moulding into car bodies, boats etc.

AMINES AND POLYAMIDES

Amines can be identified as they contain the **amino** functional group.

The **amino group** is NH_2 *Example*   1-aminopropane

Polyamides are **condensation polymers** made by reacting **diamines**, amines with two NH_2 groups, with **diacids**, carboxylic acids with two $-COOH$ groups,

e.g. **nylon** is a polyamide formed by a condensation reaction between 1,6-diaminohexane and hexan-1,6-dioc acid.

$$
\begin{array}{l}
H \\
\backslash \\
N - (CH_2)_6 - N \quad + \quad \quad C - (CH_2)_4 - C \quad + \quad N - (CH_2)_6 - N \quad + \text{ etc.} \\
/ \quad \quad \quad \quad \quad \backslash \quad H - O \quad \quad \quad O - H \quad \quad \quad \\
H \quad \quad \quad \quad \quad H
\end{array}
$$

$$
\longrightarrow \cdots N - (CH_2)_6 - N - C - (CH_2)_4 - C - N - (CH_2)_6 - N \cdots \quad + 2H_2O
$$

nylon

The polymer chain continues in both directions.

> The linking group in polyamides is called the **amide link**, i.e.
>
> $$-N-C-$$
> (with H on N and O double-bonded to C)

Nylon is a very important **engineering plastic**, where it is used in place of metal components, e.g., for machine parts.

The usefulness of nylon in engineering is due to its properties . . .
> **thermosoftening**, so it is easily moulded into complex shapes,
> **strong**, due to the **hydrogen bonds** between the **amid links** in the chains,
> **unreactive** to many chemical reagents.

SYNTHESIS GAS AND THERMOSETTING PLASTICS

Synthesis gas, a mixture of **carbon monoxide** and **hydrogen**, is formed by the **steam reforming of methane** from natural gas, or the **steam reforming of coal**,

e.g. $$CH_4 + H_2O \longrightarrow CO + H_2$$
synthesis gas

Synthesis gas is an important feedstock in a manufacturing network involving **methanol**, **methanal** and **thermosetting plastics**,

i.e.

coal   **methane**

steam
reforming

synthesis gas

The methanol cannot be produced by the hydration of an alkene, the usual method of making alkanols

methanol
CH_3OH

oxidation

methanal (+ phenol)
CH_2O

condensation
polymerisation

**thermosetting
plastics**

Methanal can form the thermosetting polymer **phenol-methanal** or **bakelite** by **condensation polymerisation** with phenol.

The oxygen on the methanal and a hydrogen from two phenol molecules are eliminated to form water. This produces links in two directions.

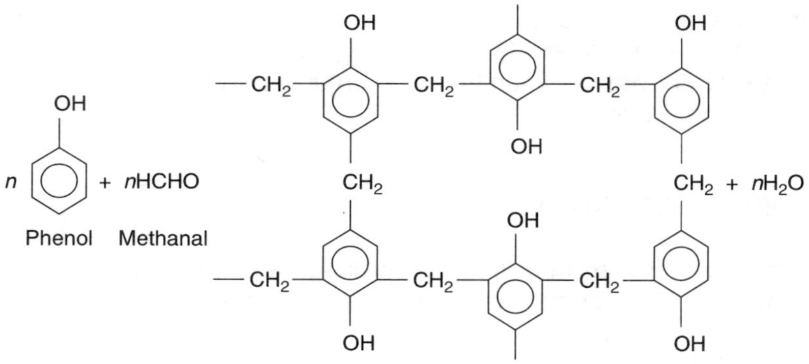

phenol methanal

or

Bakelite

The cross-links form a rigid structure, a thermosetting polymer, which does not soften on heating.

RECENT DEVELOPMENTS IN POLYMERS

KEVLAR

Kevlar is a new **aromatic polyamide** which is extremely **strong** and **light**. The delocalised electrons on the benzene ring cause the polymer chains to be rigid and they pack together in sheets, held together by hydrogen bonds between the amide links.

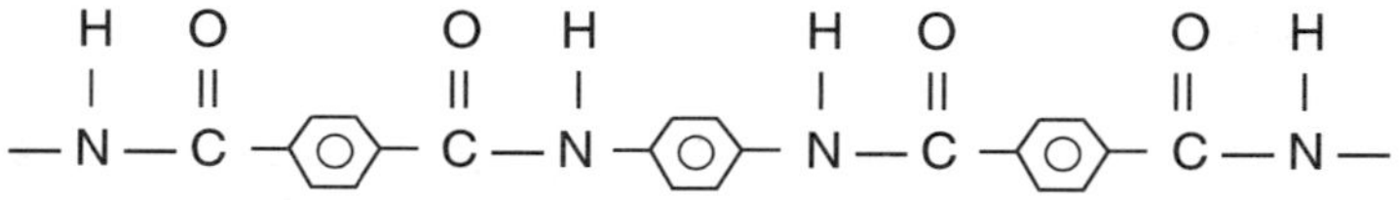

Kevlar is used for aircraft wings, bullet proof vests and other products where **strength** and **weight** are important.

POLY(ETHANOL)

Poly(ethanol) is a **soluble** polymer made by **ester exchange**, where the ethanoate groups on **poly(ethyl ethanoate)** are replaced by **methanol**.

The solubility of the polymer depends on the number of (−OH) groups attached to the chain, as these are attracted to the polar water molecules.

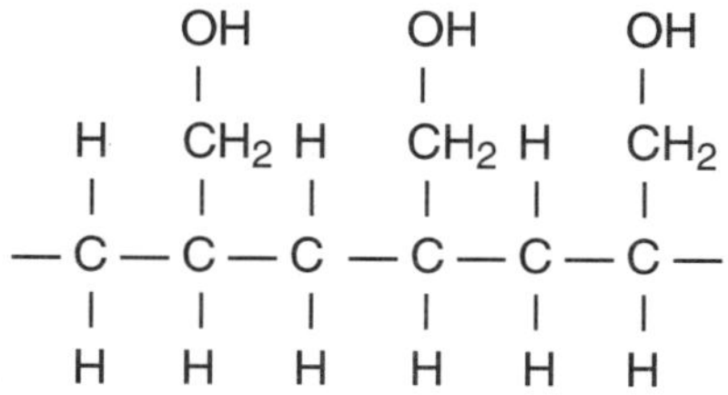

Poly(ethanol) has many applications where solubility in water is an advantage. For example, it is used for hospital laundry bags, so that soiled linen need not be handled and it is used to make dissolving stitches.

POLY(ETHYNE)

Poly(ethyne) is an addition polymer of ethyne, which has alternate single and double bonds.

The **Poly(ethyne)** chains have **delocalised electrons** along the length of their chains and it can be treated to **conduct electricity**,

i.e.

```
        H         H         H         H
        |         |         |         |
  ---C — C = C — C = C — C = C — C---
        |         |         |         |
        H         H         H         H
```

Poly(ethyne) is used as a membrane in high performance loudspeakers.

POLY(VINYL CARBOZOLE)

Poly(vinyl carbozole) is an aromatic addition polymer which shows **photoconductivity**, i.e. it **conducts** better in **light**.

Poly(vinyl carbozole) is used in some photocopiers, to produce the image.

BIODEGRADABLE POLYMERS

Biodegradable polymers can be broken down in nature.

Two types of biodegradable polymer have recently been developed.

BIOPOL

Biopol is a **polyester** made from 3-hydroxybutanoic acid which can be broken down by the action of natural **bacteria** in the soil.

```
  H                   O                        O                      O                      O
   \                 //                        ||                     ||                     ||
    O — CH — CH₂ — C      ⟶   O — CH — CH₂ — C — O — CH — CH₂ — C — O — CH — CH₂ — C —
        |             \                    |                      |                      |
        CH₃           O H                  CH₃                    CH₃                    CH₃
```

$$O-CH-CH_2-C \quad \longrightarrow \quad O-CH-CH_2-C-O-CH-CH_2-C-O-CH-CH_2-C-$$

3-hydroxybutanoic acid   **biopol**

PHOTODEGRADABLE POLYMERS

Low density polythene can be altered to include **carbonyl groups**, which make the polymer **photodegradable**, i.e. it can be broken down by **ultra-violet light**, which breaks the bond near the carbonyl groups.

Biodegradable polymers are useful for carrier bags and containers which can decay after use and so will not cause long term pollution problems.

NATURAL ORGANIC PRODUCTS

Many important compounds are derived from substances found in living things. This section deals with some of the chemistry of biologically based compounds like fats, oils, amino acids, proteins and enzymes.

At the end of this section you should be able to . . .   ✔

Name the class of chemical compounds to which *fats* and *oils* belong.   ❑
Classify fats and oils by their source.   ❑
Relate the normal states of fats and oils at room temperature to their molecular structure.   ❑
Explain how oils can be *"hardened"* and its economic importance.   ❑
State the use of fats/oils in the body and compare with carbohydrates.   ❑
Name the products of the *hydrolysis* of a fat or oil and state the number of moles of each
        product formed.   ❑
Define the term *"fatty acid"*, state the range of their molecular sizes and give their most
        common formulae.   ❑
Write the proper name and extended structural formula for *glycerol*.   ❑
Explain the terms *"trihydric alcohol"* and *"triglyceride"*.   ❑
Describe how soap is produced.   ❑
Explain the structure of a soap molecule and its cleansing action.   ❑
Explain the need for nitrogen in plant and animal life.   ❑
Identify and draw a typical *amino acid*.   ❑
Explain how *protein* molecules are formed.   ❑
Identify the *peptide link (amide link)* and describe how it is formed.   ❑
Describe how proteins are *digested* and name the chemical reaction.   ❑
Identify the structural formulae of the amino acids, given the molecular structure of a
        protein.   ❑
Explain how proteins, needed for growth, etc., are built up in the body.   ❑
Explain the term *essential amino acid*.   ❑
Describe the structure of a protein and explain the difference between *primary*,
        secondary and *tertiary* protein structures.   ❑
Explain the difference between *fibrous* and *globular protein*.   ❑
Give examples of fibrous and globular protein.   ❑
Describe how *chromatography* can be used to identify amino acids.   ❑
Describe what enzymes are and briefly explain how they work.   ❑
Explain what happens to the enzyme molecules when it is *denatured*.   ❑
Describe an investigation of factors which affect enzyme action (ppa).   ❑

WORD LIST

The following words are introduced or used in this topic. You should be able to define, use and give examples of them where appropriate.

amino acid	essential amino acid	globular protein	peptide link
carbohydrate	fats	glycerol	protein
chromatography	fatty acid	hardening	soap
denatured	fibrous protein	oils	triglyceride
enzyme			

If you are not familiar with the meaning of any of these words, you should refer to the Glossary, where these words are defined.

FATS AND OILS

The **fats** and **oils** in our diet are needed to provide **energy** for living.

Fats and **oils** can produce about **twice as much energy** as the same mass of **carbohydrate**.

Oils and fats can be classified by their source . . .

e.g. **Animal**   **Vegetable**   **Marine**

   lard   palm oil   whale oil
   suet   sunflower oil   cod liver oil

The main physical difference between fats and oils is that fats are solids at room temperature while oils are liquids, as they have lower melting points.

STRUCTURE OF FATS AND OILS

Fats and **oils** are naturally occurring **esters** formed from the alcohol **glycerol** with different **long chain carboxylic acids**,

i.e. CH_2 — OH   **Glycerol is a trihydric alcohol,**
      |
      CH — OH   it has 3 — OH groups.
      |
      CH_2 — OH   Proper name **Propan-1,2,3-triol**

The long chain carboxylic acids called **fatty acids** contain even numbers of carbon atoms ranging from C_4 to C_{24}. Most have chain lengths of C_{16} or C_{18},

e.g. $C_{17}H_{35}COOH$
stearic acid

$C_{17}H_{33}COOH$
oleic acid

The acid molecules can be saturated or unsaturated.

The fats and oils formed are called **triglycerides** as 3 moles of acid are required for each mole of alcohol,

e.g.   **CH_2OOC — R**   where **– R** represents different alkyl
      | groups, for example $C_{17}H_{35}$, or $C_{17}H_{33}$,
      CHOOC — R   from different fatty acid molecules.
      |
      CH_2OOC — R

Similar to other esters, fats and oils are formed by a **reversible reaction**. They are formed by **condensation** and broken up by **hydrolysis**.

$$\text{Fatty Acid} + \text{Glycerol} \underset{\text{hydrolysis}}{\overset{\text{condensation}}{\rightleftarrows}} \text{Fat/Oil} + \text{Water}$$

OIL OR FAT

Fats and oils usually contain a mixture of **triglycerides** with different **fatty acid** molecules combining with each **glycerol** molecule.

Oils contain more **unsaturated fatty acid**, $C = C$ double bonds, than **fats**. This can be shown as oils decolourise bromine water quicker than fats.

The high degree of **unsaturation in oils** explains their **lower melting points** as their molecules are more distorted and they **cannot pack together** as closely as molecules of fats.

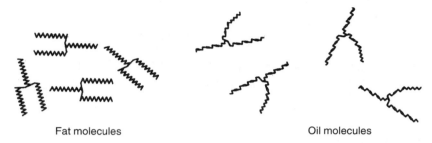

Fat molecules   Oil molecules

CONVERTING OILS TO FATS

Oils can be converted into fats by **hydrogenation**, the addition of hydrogen across the $C = C$ double bonds. This requires a **nickel catalyst** and results in the saturation of some of the double bonds in the oil molecules.

In industry this process is called the **"hardening of oils"**.

Margarine is made by **hardening vegetable oils**. The **hydrogenation** of the oil **reduces the number of double bonds** in the molecules, producing a **"hardened fat"** with a **higher melting point**.

MANUFACTURE AND ACTION OF SOAP

Soap is formed by the **alkaline hydrolysis** of fats and oils, e.g.

> **fat/oil   +   sodium hydroxide $\longrightarrow$ soap   +   glycerol**

The fat or oil is **hydrolysed** by heating with the **alkali** like sodium hydroxide. The **acid** produced is neutralised by the alkali and forms a **salt** which is the **soap**. The **glycerol** is a useful by-product.

Soap is therefore the **salt** of a **fatty acid**, for example **sodium stearate**, $C_{17}H_{33}COONa$.

The **soap molecule** is made up of a long **hydrocarbon "tail"**, which is covalent, with an **ionic "head"** at one end,

e.g. $C_{17}H_{35}COO^- \ Na^+$ Represented by . . .
                        /   \
                 covalent   ionic
                   tail   head   tail   head

This structure explains the cleansing action of soap as the covalent "tail" dissolves in grease and the ionic "head" dissolves in the water.

The grease is broken up into droplets and held in suspension in the water by the repulsion of like charges as shown below.

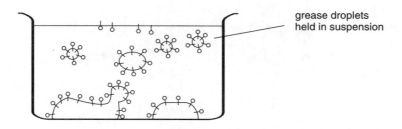

grease droplets
held in suspension

PROTEINS AND AMINO ACIDS

Nitrogen is an essential nutrient for all plants and animals as it is needed to make **proteins.**

Proteins are natural **condensation polymers** formed by joining together thousands of **amino acid** molecules.

Amino acids are a group of compounds which contain two different **functional groups** . . .

the **amino group** and the **carboxyl group**

```
 H                       O — H
  \                      /
   N —               — C
  /                      \\
 H                       O
```

The **general structure** of these amino acids can be represented by . . .

```
 H   H   O
  \  |  //
   N—C—C
  /  |   \
 H   |   O—H
     R
```

Where R represents different alkyl groups, CH_3, C_2H_5, etc. or even a — H atom.

Example

```
 H   H   O
  \  |  //
   N—C—C
  /  |   \
 H   |   O—H
   H—C—H
     |
     H
```

2-aminopropanoic acid
commonly called alanine.

MAKING PROTEINS

Proteins are formed by a **condensation reaction** between **amino acids**,

e.g.

$$
\begin{array}{ccc}
& H \quad\; H \quad\; O & \qquad\qquad H \quad\; H \quad\; O \\
& \backslash \quad\; | \quad\; / / & \qquad\qquad \backslash \quad\; | \quad\; / / \\
& N - C - C & \qquad + \qquad N - C - C \\
& / \quad\; | \quad\; \backslash & \qquad\qquad / \quad\; | \quad\; \backslash \\
& H \quad\; | \quad\; O - H & \qquad\qquad H \quad\; | \quad\; O - H \\
& \quad\; C_2H_5 & \qquad\qquad\qquad CH_3
\end{array}
$$

condensation ⟍⟍ hydrolysis

The chain can
continue at
both ends.

$$
\begin{array}{c}
H \quad\; H \quad\; O \quad\; H \quad\; H \quad\; O \\
\backslash \quad\; | \quad\; || \quad\; | \quad\; | \quad\; / / \\
N - C - C - N - C - C \qquad + \; H_2O \\
/ \quad\; | \quad\;\;\;\;\;\;\;\;\;\;\;\; | \quad\; \backslash \\
H \quad\; | \quad\;\;\;\;\;\;\;\;\;\;\;\; | \quad\; O - H \\
\quad\; C_2H_5 \qquad CH_3
\end{array}
$$

This reaction is reversible, the break up of protein molecules is called a **hydrolysis reaction** and is usually brought about by the action of enzymes.

The linking group between
each amino acid is called
a **peptide** or **amide link**.

$$
\begin{array}{c}
O \quad\; H \\
|| \quad\; | \\
- C - N -
\end{array}
$$

STRUCTURES OF PROTEIN

Proteins are made up of long chain **natural polymer** molecules, formed by joining thousands of **amino acids** together.

The structure of proteins can be described on three levels.

The **primary structure** of a **protein** is described by the **sequence** and **type** of **amino acid** present.

During **digestion**, the **proteins** we eat are broken down to their **amino acids** by a **hydrolysis reaction**. These amino acids are then taken around our body by the blood stream, where **condensation reactions** build them up, in the correct order, to produce the protein our body requires, e.g.

Hydrolysis →	Condensation →
Proteins in the food	**Amino acids**	**Protein needed by the body**

Note Our bodies cannot synthesise all **20** of the amino acids we need to make the body proteins. So we must rely on the protein in our diet for some, which are called **essential amino acids**.

Proteins form **secondary structures** due to forces of attraction between different groups in the polymer chain. For example, hydrogen bonding between every fourth $C = O$ and $— NH$ group in certain protein chains cause them to twist and form a spiral shape, e.g.

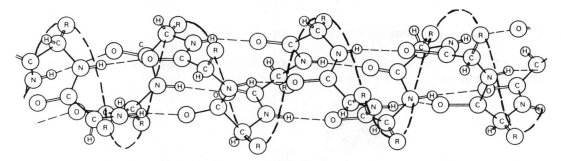

The α-helix is the most common secondary structure in proteins

Finally, intermolecular bonding between the carboxyl and amino groups in the protein chains can produce two types of **tertiary structure**.

Fibrous proteins are structures which have the spiral chains folded to form **long**, **thin** shapes. These are **strong** and generally **insoluble** in water. Fibrous proteins make up the major structural material of **animal tissue**, for example, **hair**, **skin**, **tendons** and **muscle**.

Globular proteins have their spiral chains folded into **spherical** shapes. They are generally **soluble** in water and are often involved in maintaining and regulating the **processes of life**. For example, **haemoglobin**, **enzymes** and certain **hormones** like **insulin** are all globular proteins.

CHROMATOGRAPHY

Chromatography is a technique for **separating** and **identifying** mixtures and it can be used to identify the **amino acids** formed by the **hydrolysis** of a **protein**.

The **hydrolysed protein** is spotted onto some chromatography paper along with a number of **known amino acids**. The paper is then placed in a suitable solvent.

As the solvent soaks up the paper, the amino acids climb to different levels depending on their solubility in the solvent.

When the chromatogram is developed, the distance the spots have moved up the paper will identify the amino acids in the protein.

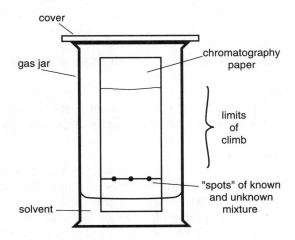

HOW ENZYMES WORK

Enzymes are soluble **globular protein** molecules which act as **catalysts** in **biological** reactions.

The **shape** of the **enzyme molecule** is very important in its action.

It is thought that the structure of the enzyme "fits" the shape of the reactant molecule like a **"key in a lock"** and this brings about the chemical change, e.g.

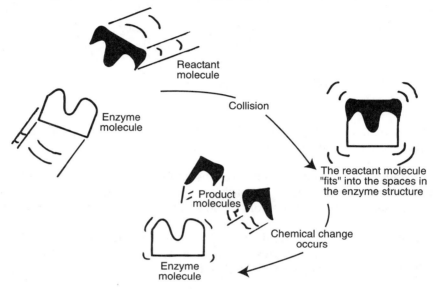

Each **enzyme** is **specific**, it can only effect one particular change, as only one type of molecule will "fit" its structure.

Enzymes work best within a narrow range of **pH** and **temperatures**, as changes in these conditions can effect the **shape** of the enzyme molecule.

When the **shape** of a enzyme molecule is **changed** in this way, we say it has been **denatured**. The denatured enzyme does not work as it no longer "fits" the reactant molecules.

Investigating factors which affect enzyme action

Aim
To investigate the effect of pH and temperature changes on the activity of the enzyme catalase, which speeds up the decomposition of hydrogen peroxide producing oxygen gas.

Method
The apparatus is set up as shown opposite. A piece of raw potato (a source of catalase) is added to the   hydrogen peroxide solution. Oxygen gas is produced and the number of bubbles of oxygen formed is counted over a set time interval.

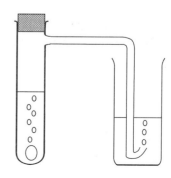

The experiment is repeated, controlling all the variables, except either the **temperature** or the **pH of the solution**.

Results

The rate of the reaction is proportional to the number of bubbles of oxygen gas produced in a set time interval. Therefore graphs of number of bubbles against either temperature or pH would show their effect on the enzyme activity.

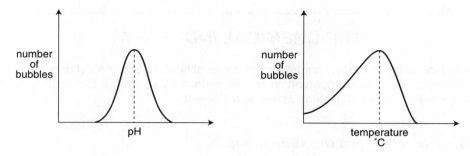

Conclusions

This particular enzyme works best at a **pH of 7** and a temperature of **40 °C**.

It can be seen from the graphs that if the pH or temperature is raised or lowered from these values, the enzyme action is less efficient.

UNIT 3
CHEMICAL REACTIONS

THE CHEMICAL INDUSTRY

The **chemical industry** is a major contributor to our quality of life and the national economy. This section considers the stages involved in the manufacture of products within the chemical industry, including issues such as cost, safety and efficiency.

At the end of this section you should be able to . . .   ✔

Describe some ways in which the *chemical industry* is important to our lives and the
     national economy. ❐
State some uses of the major products of the chemical industry. ❐
Name the major raw materials used in the chemical industry. ❐
Explain the term *feedstock*. ❐
State the main stages involved in the manufacture of a new product. ❐
State the main manufacturing costs in the chemical industry. ❐
Explain the terms *capital*, *fixed* and *variable costs*. ❐
Explain how energy efficiency can be increased and its importance. ❐
Name some examples of feedstocks and raw materials used in particular processes. ❐
Describe examples of the steps involved in a chemical manufacturing process. ❐
Explain the advantages and disadvantages of *batch* and *continuous processes*. ❐
Discuss the chemical route and process chosen to manufacture a product in terms of
     economics. ❐
Explain the importance of safety and environmental issues in the chemical industry. ❐
Describe factors which affect the location of a chemical industry. ❐

WORD LIST

The following words are introduced or used in this topic. You should be able to define, use and give examples of them where appropriate.

batch process	feedstock	variable costs
capital costs	fixed costs	
continuous process	raw materials	

If you are not familiar with the meaning of any of these words, you should refer to the Glossary, where these words are defined.

THE CHEMICAL INDUSTRY

Since the age of the industrial revolution and the onset of making products like bleaches, dyes, acids and alkalis on a large scale, the **chemical industry** has been of major importance to Scotland and the UK.

The basis of the **chemical industry** is to make a **profit** by changing **raw materials** into **feedstocks** and **consumer products**.

Note   A **feedstock** is a substance or mixture of substances from which other chemicals can be extracted or synthesised.

The main **raw materials** for the chemical industry are . . .
>   **fossil fuels** (coal, oil and gas),
>   **metal ores** and **minerals**,
>   **air** and **water**.

The **use** of the many **consumer products** made by the **chemical industry** have greatly improved the quality of our lives, e.g.

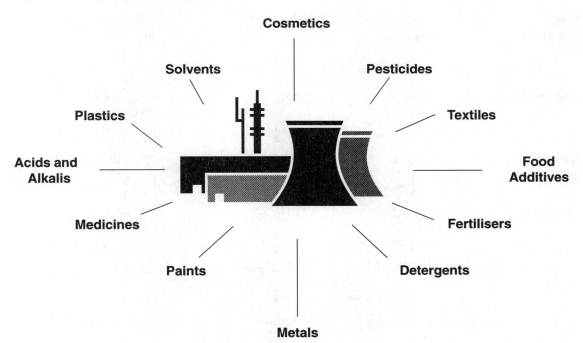

The **chemical industry** is also a major contributor to the **economy** of Scotland and the UK, as it is . . .

>   the fourth largest **manufacturing industry**,
>   the **largest export** earner of any industry.

DEVELOPING NEW PRODUCTS

New materials are continually being developed by the chemical industry. The main **stages** in the manufacture of a new product include . . .

- **Research**   To find out about the structure, properties and methods of preparation of the new material.
- **Pilot Study**   To investigate the possible processes and routes for the manufacture of the new material.
- **Scaling-up**   A test production to find the best possible conditions for full scale production.
- **Production**   The setting up and running of the full scale production plant under controlled conditions.
- **Review**   A evaluation of the industrial process to see if it is possible to improve efficiency, profit or safety.

MANUFACTURING PROCESSES AND ROUTES

The manufacture of most chemical products involve a **series of steps**, involving processes or chemical reactions, which start with the **raw materials** and ending with a **consumer product**, e.g.

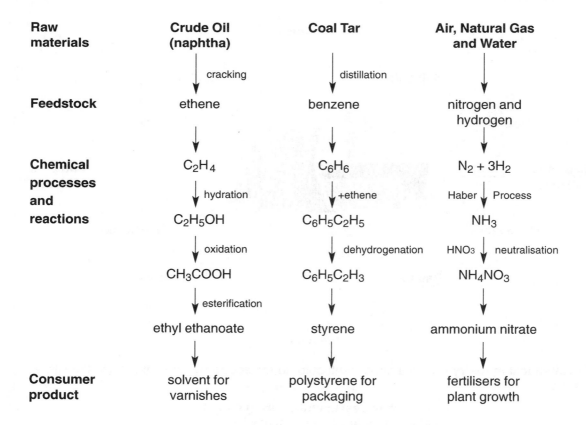

Raw materials	**Crude Oil (naphtha)**	**Coal Tar**	**Air, Natural Gas and Water**
	↓ cracking	↓ distillation	↓
Feedstock	ethene	benzene	nitrogen and hydrogen
	↓	↓	↓
Chemical processes and reactions	C_2H_4	C_6H_6	$N_2 + 3H_2$
	↓ hydration	↓ +ethene	Haber ↓ Process
	C_2H_5OH	$C_6H_5C_2H_5$	NH_3
	↓ oxidation	↓ dehydrogenation	HNO_3 ↓ neutralisation
	CH_3COOH	$C_6H_5C_2H_3$	NH_4NO_3
	↓ esterification	↓	↓
	ethyl ethanoate	styrene	ammonium nitrate
	↓	↓	↓
Consumer product	solvent for varnishes	polystyrene for packaging	fertilisers for plant growth

TYPES OF PROCESS

The manufacture of chemical products may be organised in a **batch** or **continuous process**, the choice is usually a question of **scale**.

Batch processes are used to make **small amounts** of product, like pharmaceuticals and cosmetics.

In a batch process the raw materials are mixed together in a reactor vessel and the product is separated from the mixture when the reactions are complete.

The plant is more **flexible** and can often be used to make several different products but it is usually **more labour intensive**.

Continuous processes are used to make **large amounts** of product, like the **bulk chemicals**, ammonia, sulphuric acid and nitric acid.

In a continuous process, the raw materials are fed in at one end of the plant and the product is formed continually, 24 hours a day.

A continuous process is **less labour intensive** and generally more **efficient** than a batch process. However, the plant can only be used to make one particular product and it is often **difficult** and expensive to **shut down** for repair and maintenance.

MANUFACTURING COSTS

The main manufacturing costs in the chemical industry come under three headings . . .

- **Capital costs** are the initial expenses needed to set up the process. These include the purchase of land, buildings, plant and machinery.
- **Fixed costs** are constant and don't change with the level of production. These include depreciation of plant, maintenance, research and development and staff wages.
- **Variable costs** increase as production increases. These include the cost of raw materials, distribution and energy.

The chemical industry is generally **capital intensive** rather than **labour intensive**. Most chemical industries are very expensive to set up but need few operators to maintain production.

Energy Costs

Energy costs can be high and the **efficient** use of **energy** is essential to **economic** success in the chemical industry.

The use of **heat exchangers** improves **energy efficiency** as these remove unwanted heat from energy producing (exothermic) processes so it can be used in energy consuming processes like distillation.

MANUFACTURING ROUTES AND CONDITIONS

The **routes** and **conditions** used for the manufacture of a chemical will always be chosen to maximise economic **efficiency**.

The following questions may be important in this choice.

> What are the costs of different suitable **feedstocks**?
> What **yield** of product can be obtained?
> Is a **catalyst** available and what does it cost?
> Do the **by-products** have any economic use?
> Can reactants or by-products be **recycled**?
> Which route makes the most efficient use of **energy**?
> Will a **batch** or **continuous** process be most suitable?

The choice of route and process will also consider **safety** and **environmental issues**. Many chemical substances are potentially hazardous to humans and can cause pollution. Hence the use and disposal of all chemical substances have to be controlled according to government **"Health and Safety"** regulations.

LOCATION OF CHEMICAL INDUSTRY

The **location** of a **chemical industry** will depend on a number of factors, not all of which are chemical in nature, including . . .

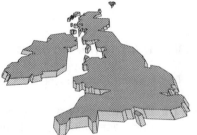

> Availability of **raw materials** and **energy** sources.
> **Transport** links and distance to **markets** for products.
> Availability of skilled **labour** and facilities.
> **Historical** reasons for manufacture to continue in an area.
> Availability of development **grants**, reduced rates, etc.
> Effects on the environment, possible **pollution** problems.

HESS'S LAW

Thermochemistry is the study of the energy changes which occur during chemical reactions. This section extends our understanding of enthalpy changes and introduces Hess's Law, and some of its applications.

At the end of this section you should be able to . . . ✔

State Hess's Law. ☐
Explain Hess's Law by using the enthalpy changes for appropriate chemical reactions. ☐
Describe how Hess's Law can be confirmed by experiment *(ppa)*. ☐
Calculate the enthalpy change (ΔH) of reactions by using Hess's Law. ☐

WORD LIST

The following words are introduced or used in this topic. You should be able to define, use and give examples of them where appropriate.

enthalpy of combustion   enthalpy of neutralisation   Hess's Law
enthalpy of formation   enthalpy of solution   kilojoules

If you are not familiar with the meaning of any of these words, you should refer to the Glossary, where these words are defined.

HESS'S LAW AND ENTHALPY CALCULATIONS

The **enthalpy change** — ΔH — during a chemical reaction is the difference between the enthalpy of the reactants and the enthalpy of the products.

$$\Delta H \ = \ H(\text{products}) - H(\text{reactants})$$

Hess's Law states that the **enthalpy change** for a chemical reaction is **independent** of the **route** taken,

e.g. Consider the reaction of carbon with oxygen to produce carbon dioxide. This can be brought about by two possible routes.

Route 1 $C\,(s) + O_2\,(g) \quad \rightarrow \quad CO_2\,(g) \quad \Delta H_1 = -394kJ$
(1 stage)

Route 2 $C\,(s) + \frac{1}{2}O_2\,(g) \quad \rightarrow \quad CO\,(g) \quad \Delta H_2 = -111kJ$
(2 stages) $CO\,(g) + \frac{1}{2}O_2\,(g) \quad \rightarrow \quad CO_2\,(g) \quad \Delta H_3 = -283kJ$

Note that the enthalpy change in route 1 is equal to the sum of the two enthalpy changes in route 2 (−394kJ).

$$\begin{aligned}
\Delta H_1 \ &= \ \Delta H_2 \ + \ \Delta H_3 \\
-394kJ \ &= \ -111kJ \ + \ -283kJ \\
&= \ -394kJ
\end{aligned}$$

Investigating Hess's Law

Aim

To use the neutralisation reaction between potassium hydroxide and hydrochloric acid, to confirm Hess's Law.
This reaction has two possible routes.

i.e.

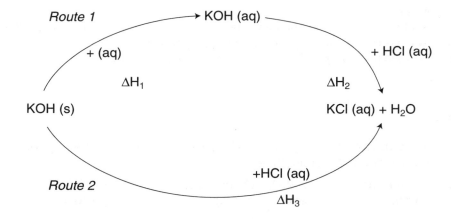

Method

● Measure the temperature rise (Δt) when . . .
  1·2g of KOH(s) is added to 25 cm^3 of water   = Δt_1
  the KOH(aq) is added to 25 cm^3 1 mol l^{-1} HCl(aq)   = Δt_2 *Route 1*
  1·2g KOH(s) is added to 25 cm^3 1 mol l^{-1} HCl(aq)   = Δt_3 *Route 2*

● Calculate the enthalpy changes, ΔH, for each stage in the two routes by using,
$$E_h = -\,c.m.\,\Delta t$$
  and finding the energy released per mole.

Results and Conclusions

Calculations should show that $\Delta H_1 + \Delta H_2 = \Delta H_3$

confirming Hess's Law that the overall energy change is independent of the route taken.

USING HESS'S LAW

Hess's Law can be used to **calculate** unknown **enthalpy changes** which are either difficult or impossible to find by experiment.

One method used to calculate an **enthalpy change** involves **rearranging** a set of given reaction **equations** with known ΔH values.

The following rules should be used when manipulating enthalpy changes ...

- ΔH **is independent of the route taken — Hess's Law.**
- ΔH **is proportional to the quantities of reactants and products.**
- **Reverse a reaction equation and change the sign on the ΔH.**

The most common type of Hess's Law calculation involves finding **enthalpies of formation** from enthalpies of combustion of the compound and its elements.

Enthalpy of Formation

The ΔH_f – of a substance is the energy released or absorbed when 1 mole of the substance is formed from its elements in their normal states, e.g.

The enthalpy of formation for ethanol is the energy change associated with the reaction . . .

$$2C\ (s)\ +\ 3H_2\ (g)\ +\ \tfrac{1}{2}O_2\ (g)\ \rightarrow\ \underset{\text{1 mole}}{C_2H_6O\ (l)}$$

Example

Calculate the enthalpy of formation of propanol using the data on enthalpies of combustion in the data book.

Given combustion equations, ΔH from data books . . .

		ΔH/kJ mol^{-1}
①	$C\ (s)\ +\ O_2\ (g)\ \rightarrow\ CO_2$	−394
②	$H_2\ (g)\ +\ \tfrac{1}{2}O_2(g)\ \rightarrow\ H_2O\ (l)$	−286
③	$C_3H_8O\ (l)\ +\ 4\tfrac{1}{2}O_2(g)\ \rightarrow\ 3CO_2\ (g)\ +\ 4H_2O\ (l)$	−2010

The "target equation" is the enthalpy of formation of propanol . . .

$$3C\ (s)\ +\ 4H_2\ (g)\ +\ \tfrac{1}{2}O_2\ (g)\ \rightarrow\ C_3H_8O\ (l) \qquad \Delta HF\ =\ ?$$

Rearrange the given equations to get each component of the "target equation" . . .

① × 3	$3C\ (s)\ +\ 3O_2\ (g)\ \rightarrow\ 3CO_2$	−1182
② × 4	$4H_2\ (g)\ +\ 2O_2\ (g)\ \rightarrow\ 4H_2O\ (l)$	−1144
③ reversed	$3CO_2\ (g)\ +\ 4H_2O\ (l)\ \rightarrow\ C_3H_8O\ (l)\ +\ 4\tfrac{1}{2}O_2\ (g)$	+2010

Add the three equation and enthalpy changes together and cancel the components which are the same on each side.
This should give the "target equation" . . .

$$3C\ (s)\ +\ 4H_2\ (g)\ +\ \tfrac{1}{2}O_2\ (g)\ \rightarrow\ C_3H_8O\ (l) \qquad −316$$

Therefore the enthalpy of formation of propanol is −316 kJ mol^{-1}.

EQUILIBRIUM

Many chemical reactions do not go to completion but reach a state of **equilibrium** where both reactants and products exist together.

This section introduces the concept of equilibrium and considers how it is affected by changes in conditions.

At the end of this section you should be able to . . .   ✔

Explain the term *dynamic equilibrium*.   ❐
Explain the *equilibrium position* in terms of the rates of the forward and back reactions.   ❐
State what happens to the concentration of reactants and products after equilibrium is
    attained.   ❐
Explain the effect of changing concentrations, temperature and pressure on the position
    of equilibrium.   ❐
Describe the effect of a catalyst on an equilibrium.   ❐
Explain the choice of condition in the Haber Process, in terms of the ammonia yield and
    economics.   ❐
Explain why unreacted nitrogen and hydrogen are recycled in the Haber Process.   ❐

WORD LIST

The following words are introduced or used in this topic. You should be able to define, use and give examples of them where appropriate.

dynamic equilibrium   Haber process   reversible reaction

If you are not familiar with the meaning of any of these words, you should refer to the Glossary, where these words are defined.

DYNAMIC EQUILIBRIUM

Many chemical reactions are **reversible**.

In these reactions there is a **forward** and a **back reaction**, as the products once formed can react to re-form the reactants.

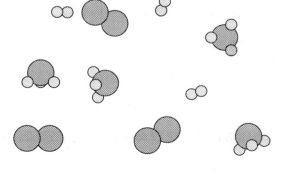

e.g.
$$N_2 + 3H_2 \underset{\text{back}}{\overset{\text{forward}}{\rightleftharpoons}} 2NH_3$$

The sign $\rightleftharpoons$ means that the reaction goes in both directions. In a reversible reaction you can never get 100% products formed and will always have a mixture of reactants and products.

Consider how the **rate** of the **forward** and **back reactions** change as a reversible reaction proceeds . . .

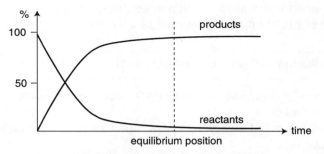

The position of equilibrium can vary from 1% to 99% of products.

As the **forward reaction slows down** the **back reaction speeds up** until they are both taking place at the **same rate**. This is called the **equilibrium position**. After this point is reached the percentage of **reactant** and **product** will stay **constant**.

This is a **dynamic equilibrium** as both forward and back reactions continue.

Consider the equilibrium which can be set up between two iodine solutions, one in chloroform and one in water,

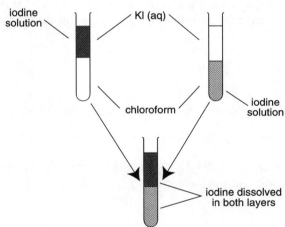

In both cases the same position of equilibrium is reached with iodine moving up and down between the layers at the same rate.

This means that the same equilibrium position is reached from either side of the process, i.e.

$$A + B \rightleftharpoons C + D$$
is the same as
$$C + D \rightleftharpoons A + B$$

Note   **Equilibrium** can only be established in a **closed system** where the reaction is carried out in a sealed container and none of the reactants or products are lost.

In an **open system**, equilibrium cannot be established due to loss of some reactant or product, e.g.

If calcium carbonate is heated in an open test-tube, the reaction goes to completion as the carbon dioxide escapes, the back reaction cannot occur.

$$CaCO_3(s) \rightarrow CaO(s) + CO_2(g)$$

FACTORS AFFECTING THE EQUILIBRIUM POSITION

It can be shown that, in most cases, when a chemical reaction in **equilibrium** is subjected to a **change** in conditions the **equilibrium shifts** to **oppose** or **minimise** the effect of the change, i.e.

CHANGE in CONDITION	Equilibrium moves in direction which . . .
Increase concentration	removes the substance which was added and decreases its concentration.
Decrease concentration	forms the substance which was removed and increases its concentration.
Increase pressure	forms less gas molecules as this reduces the pressure.
Decrease pressure	forms more gas molecules as this increases the pressure.
Increase temperature	is endothermic as this will take in heat energy and lower the temperature.
Decrease temperature	is exothermic as this will give out heat energy and raise the temperature.

The examples which follow show how the position of equilibrium, and thus the equilibrium mixture, in a reversible reaction can be affected by changes in **concentration**, **pressure** and **temperature**.

Concentration

When ethanoic acid is dissolved in water the following equilibrium is established.

$$CH_3COOH \text{ (aq)} \rightleftharpoons CH_3COO^- \text{ (aq)} + H^+ \text{ (aq)}$$

If some solid sodium ethanoate ($Na^+ CH_3COO^-$) is added, the concentration of CH_3COO^- (aq) ions is increased and the equilibrium will shift to the LHS, to reduce the concentration of CH_3COO^- (aq) ions, i.e.,

CH_3COO^- (aq) and H^+ (aq) will join together to form more CH_3COOH(aq).

Notice that this shift in equilibrium position will also reduce the concentration of H^+ (aq) ions so the pH of the solution will increase.

Pressure

The initial step in the manufacture of sulphuric acid involves the oxidation of sulphur dioxide by the following equilibrium reaction.

$$2SO_2 \text{ (g)} + O_2 \text{ (g)} \rightleftharpoons 2SO_3 \text{ (g)}$$

If pressure is increased, the equilibrium will move in the direction which results in a lower gas volume and reduced pressure, i.e. to the side which forms less gas molecules.

In this case this means that at higher pressure the equilibrium moves to the RHS and more sulphur trioxide is formed.

Note Pressure can only affect reactions which involve a change in the number of gas molecules from reactants to products, e.g.

$$H_2\,(g)\ +\ I_2\,(g) \rightleftharpoons 2HI(g)$$

This equilibrium is not affected by pressure, as the number of gas molecules are the same on each side of the equation.

Temperature

The gas nitrogen dioxide exists in equilibrium with the gas dinitrogen tetroxide.

$$\Delta H_{back} \quad +ve \qquad 2NO_2\,(g) \rightleftharpoons N_2O_4(g) \qquad \Delta H_{forward} \quad -ve$$
$$\text{endothermic} \qquad\quad \text{brown} \qquad \text{colourless} \qquad\quad \text{exothermic}$$

If the temperature is raised, the equilibrium will move in the direction which absorbs heat, i.e. the endothermic direction (ΔH +ve), as this will lower the temperature.

In this case the equilibrium moves to the LHS, at higher temperatures, more nitrogen dioxide is formed and the mixture becomes darker brown in colour.

CATALYSTS AND EQUILIBRIUM

Catalysts speed up chemical reactions without being permanently changed.

Catalysts work by **lowering** the **activation energy** so more molecules will react when they collide.

In equilibrium reactions the catalyst speeds up the **forward** and the **back reaction** by the same amount.

Catalysts have no effect on the position of equilibrium.

With a catalyst, equilibrium is reached more **quickly**.

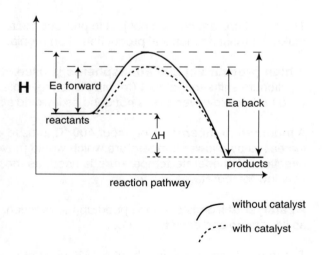

EQUILIBRIUM IN INDUSTRY

Consider the manufacture of **ammonia** by the **Haber Process**.

Ammonia is formed by a **reversible reaction**, the equilibrium is . . .

$$N_2\,(g)\ +\ 3H_2\,(g)\ \rightleftharpoons\ 2NH_3\,(g)\quad \Delta H_{forward}\ -ve$$
$$\text{exothermic}$$

The forward reaction and a high yield of ammonia will be favoured by a **high pressure** and a **low temperature**.

Flow diagram of the Haber Process

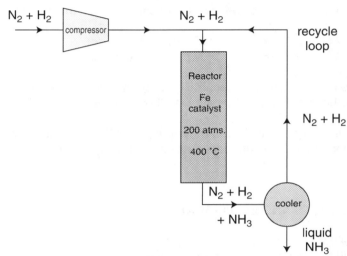

The conditions are chosen not just to produce the fastest rate of reaction and highest yields but to make the most economical production of ammonia.

A **high pressure** of **200 atmospheres** is used, this increases the yield of ammonia, as the equilibrium shifts to the right (forming less gas molecules). A higher pressure would increase the yield further. However, this is not done as it would also increase the capital and running costs.

A **moderate temperature** of about **400 °C** is used even though the yield of ammonia would be increased by a lower temperature which would move the equilibrium to the right (the exothermic direction). A moderate temperature is used, as the formation of ammonia would be too slow at very low temperatures.

A **catalyst of iron** is used to speed up the reaction. Platinum is a better catalyst but iron is used as it is cheap and easy to replace.

These conditions produce about a 15% yield of ammonia, which is removed as it is formed, by **cooling** and **liquefying**. The unreacted nitrogen and hydrogen are **recycled**, so that none of the reactants are wasted, even if equilibrium is not reached.

ACIDS AND BASES

Acids and **bases** play an important part in our everyday lives as well as the chemical industry. This section takes a closer look at the relationship between pH, ion concentrations and the equilibrium in water, acids and alkalis. It also considers the different types of acid, alkali and salt which can be produced.

At the end of this section you should be able to . . .   ✔

Describe the pH scale and state its range of values.   ❒

Relate integral values of pH to the concentration of H^+ ions in mol l^{-1}.   ❒

Describe a pH of 7 in terms of concentration of H^+ and OH^- ions.   ❒

Calculate the concentration of H^+ ions in a solution from the concentration of OH^- ions,
    and vice versa.   ❒

Describe the equilibrium which exists in pure water and all solutions.   ❒

Explain the difference between strong and weak acids.   ❒

Explain the properties of acids dissolved in different solvents.   ❒

Describe the differences in properties between solutions of strong and weak acids of the
    same concentration.   ❒

Explain, using equations, the equilibrium in solutions of ethanoic acid, sulphur dioxide
    and carbon dioxide.   ❒

Describe how you could estimate the relative strength of weak acids.   ❒

Explain the difference between strong and weak alkalis.   ❒

Describe the differences in properties between solutions of strong and weak alkalis of the
    same concentration.   ❒

Explain, using equations, the equilibrium in solutions of ammonia.   ❒

Describe the nature of a salt solution, given the strength of the acid and base used to
    make the salt.   ❒

Explain the pH of soap solution by reference to its structure.   ❒

Explain the pH of salt solutions by reference to the appropriate equilibrium reaction
    equations.   ❒

WORD LIST

The following words are introduced or used in this topic. You should be able to define, use and give examples of them where appropriate.

acid	ionic product of water	strong acid
acid rain	neutralisation	strong alkali
alkali	pH scale	weak acid
amine	salt	weak alkali
base	soap	

If you are not familiar with the meaning of any of these words, you should refer to the Glossary, where these words are defined.

THE pH SCALE

The **pH of a solution**, which can be found using an indicator or a pH meter, is used as a measure of **acidity** or **alkalinity**.

The **pH scale** is a continuous range from **below 0 to above 14** and is related to the **concentration of H^+ ions** and **OH^- ions** present.

The pH scale

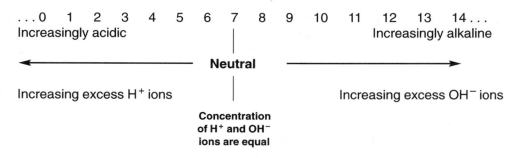

ACIDS, BASES AND ALKALIS

Acids, **bases** and **alkalis** are very common substances which take part in many chemical reactions and have many uses.

The main properties of **acids** are . . .

> Contain **excess H$^+$** ions in solution.
> Solutions have a **pH** of **less than 7**.
> Solutions **conduct electricity** as ions are present.
> Donate **H$^+$ ions** in **neutralisation reactions** with **bases**, e.g.,
> > Metal + acid $\rightarrow$ salt + hydrogen.
> > Metal oxide + acid $\rightarrow$ salt + water.
> > Metal hydroxide + acid $\rightarrow$ salt + water.
> > Metal carbonate + acid $\rightarrow$ salt + water + carbon dioxide.

The main properties of **bases** are . . .

> React with **acids**.
> Combine with **H$^+$ ions** in **neutralisation reactions**.
> **Soluble bases** are called **alkalis**.
> Solutions have a **pH greater than 7**.
> If soluble they form **excess OH$^-$ ions**.
> Solutions can **conduct electricity** as **ions** are present.

Examples   **Metals**, **metal oxides**, **hydroxides** and **carbonates**.

EQUILIBRIUM IN WATER

Pure water conducts electricity very slightly due to an equilibrium in which a few water molecules split up into ions.

The **equilibrium in water** is . . .

$$H_2O \rightleftharpoons H^+ (aq) + OH^- (aq)$$

The equilibrium forms **equal concentrations** of H$^+$ ions and OH$^-$ ions.

The **concentration of H$^+$ and OH$^-$ ions** at 25 °C is 10^{-7} **mol** l^{-1}.

$\therefore$ In pure water . . .

$$[H^+] \times [OH^-] = (10^{-7}) \times (10^{-7})$$
$$= 10^{-14} \text{ mol}^2 \ l^{-2}$$

Note   [ ] means "concentration of" in mol l^{-1}.

Now all solutions, acidic, alkaline or neutral, will contain some H$^+$ ions and OH$^-$ ions due to the equilibrium in water and it has been found that, in all solutions, $[H^+] \times [OH^-] = 10^{-14}$ **mol**^{2} l^{-2}, i.e.

> 10^{-14} **mol**^{2} l^{-2} is a **constant** called "**The Ionic Product of Water**"

pH, ACIDS AND H$^+$ ION CONCENTRATION

Consider the pH of a range of acid solutions.
Starting with 0·1 mol l^{-1} hydrochloric acid and diluting by 10 each time.

Conc. of HCl	[H$^+$] mol l^{-1}	pH
0·1	10^{-1}	1
0·01	10^{-2}	2
0·001	10^{-3}	3
0·0001	10^{-4}	4
0·00001	10^{-5}	5
0·000001	10^{-6}	6
0·0000001	10^{-7}	7

From these results we can see that for an acid . . .
pH = − power of 10 of [H$^+$]

THE pH SCALE AND ALKALIS

We can use the **ionic product of water** to calculate the [H$^+$] and thus the **pH** of an **alkaline solution** of known [OH$^-$], i.e.

As $[H^+] \times [OH^-] = 10^{-14}$

Then $[H^+] = \dfrac{10^{-14}}{[OH^-]}$ for any solution

Example

What is the pH of a 0·1 mol l^{-1} solution of sodium hydroxide?

0·1 mol l^{-1} NaOH has a [OH$^-$] = 10^{-1}

As $[H^+]$ $= \dfrac{10^{-14}}{[OH^-]}$

$= \dfrac{10^{-14}}{10^{-1}}$

$= 10^{-13}$

Now   pH   = − power of 10 of [H$^+$]

$\therefore$ **pH of 0·1 mol l^{-1} NaOH = 13**

Consider the concentrations of OH^- ions, H^+ ions and the pH of a range of alkaline solutions. Starting with 0.1 mol l^{-1} sodium hydroxide and diluting by 10 each time.

Conc. of NaOH	$[OH^-]$ mol l^{-1}	$[H^+]$ mol l^{-1}	pH	
0.1	10^{-1}	10^{-13}	13	These results also show
0.01	10^{-2}	10^{-12}	12	that for an alkali . . .
0.001	10^{-3}	10^{-11}	11	**pH = – power of 10 of $[H^+]$**
0.0001	10^{-4}	10^{-10}	10	
0.00001	10^{-5}	10^{-9}	9	
0.000001	10^{-6}	10^{-8}	8	
0.0000001	10^{-7}	10^{-7}	7	

> Therefore the **pH** for **all solutions** in water is equal to . . .
> the **negative** of the **power of 10** of the **hydrogen ion concentration**.

Note   A change in pH of **1 unit** represents a **10 fold** change in the concentration of H^+ and OH^- ions.

A change in pH of **2 units** represents a **100 fold** change in the concentration of H^+ and OH^- ions, etc.

STRONG AND WEAK ACIDS

Acids can be classified into **two groups** depending on how they dissolve in **water**.

Strong acids dissolve by **completely breaking up** into **ions**, e.g.	**Weak acids** do **not ionise completely** in solution, e.g.
$HCl \rightarrow H^+ (aq) + Cl^- (aq)$	$CH_3COOH(aq) \rightleftharpoons CH_3COO^- (aq) + H^+(aq)$
Hydrochloric acid solution contains only H^+ and Cl^- ions.	Ethanoic acid solutions contain molecules of CH_3COOH as well as H^+ and CH_3COO^- ions.
Examples of strong acids . . .	Examples of weak acids . . .
Hydrochloric acid (HCl)	Ethanoic acid (CH_3COOH)
Nitric acid (HNO_3)	Methanoic acid (HCOOH)
Sulphuric acid (H_2SO_4)	Sulphurous acid (H_2SO_3)
Hydrofluoric acid (HF)	Carbonic acid (H_2CO_3)

Weak acids are found in nature as well as in industry. Here are some examples of important weak acid equilibrium reactions.

A weak acid equilibrium is set up when carbon dioxide dissolves in water.

$$CO_2 (aq) + H_2O (l) \rightleftharpoons 2H^+ (aq) + CO_3 (aq)$$
$$\text{carbonic acid}$$

This equilibrium occurs in rain water and fizzy drinks, to make them acidic.

Air polluted with sulphur dioxide makes the rain even more acidic, as another weak acid equilibrium is set up.

$$SO_2 \text{ (aq)} + H_2O \text{ (}l\text{)} \rightleftharpoons 2H^+ \text{ (aq)} + SO_3^{2-} \text{ (aq)}$$
sulphurous acid

This type of "acid rain" causes major environmental problems.

SOLVENTS FOR ACIDS

Acid properties are affected by the **type** of **solvent** used to form the solution, e.g.

> **Hydrogen chloride** dissolved in **carbon tetrachloride** is **not** an **acid** as the HCl molecules do **not break up into ions** in the **non-polar solvent**. Therefore this solution **does not** contain **H^+ ions**, **conduct electricity** or **react** with **metals**.

A **polar solvent** like **water** is needed to show **acidic properties**.

STRONG AND WEAK BASES

Bases or **alkalis** can also be classified into **two groups**, depending on how they dissolve in water.

Strong bases/alkalis dissolve by **breaking up completely** into **ions** in solution, e.g.	**Weak bases/alkalis** do **not ionise completely** in solution, e.g.
$NaOH \text{ (s)} + \text{(aq)} \rightarrow Na^+ \text{ (aq)} + OH^- \text{ (aq)}$	$NH_3\text{(aq)} + H_2O\text{(}l\text{)} \rightleftharpoons NH_4^+ \text{ (aq)} + OH^- \text{ (aq)}$
Sodium hydroxide solution contains only Na^+ and OH^- ions.	Ammonia solution contains molecules of NH_3 as well as OH^- and NH_4^+ ions.

Examples of strong bases . . .
    Sodium hydroxide (NaOH)
    Potassium hydroxide (KOH)
    Lithium hydroxide (LiOH)
	Examples of weak bases . . .
	    Ammonia (NH_3)
	    Aminomethane (CH_3NH_2)
	    Aminoethane ($C_2H_5NH_2$)

Note   Amines are a group of organic compounds which contain the $-NH_2$ group. They are related to ammonia and react similarly.

PROPERTIES OF STRONG AND WEAK ACIDS AND ALKALIS

Equimolar solutions of strong and weak acids and strong and weak alkalis differ in **conductivity**, **pH** and **speed of reaction**.

The difference in properties is due to the different concentrations of H^+ and OH^- ions in the solutions.

The properties of strong and weak acids can be tested using 0.1 mol l^{-1} solutions of hydrochloric acid and ethanoic acid.

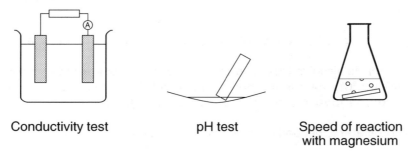

| Conductivity test | pH test | Speed of reaction with magnesium |

Comparing solutions of equal concentration, the **stronger acid** will have a . . .

higher conductivity, lower pH and faster reaction

. . . as the stronger the acid the higher the H^+ ion concentration.

The **strength** of **bases/alkalis** will also affect their properties for the same reasons.

The **stronger base/alkali** will have a . . .

higher conductivity and higher pH

. . . as they will contain a higher concentration of OH^- ions.

Neutralisation Reactions of Acids and Alkalis

The amount of acid or alkali required for neutralisation depends on the **concentrations** of the solutions and the **number** of replaceable H^+ and OH^- **ions** in the formulae of the acid and alkali.

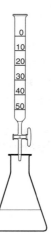

The **strength** of the acid or alkali does **not** affect the **amounts** of each required for neutralisation, e.g.,

Sulphuric acid (H_2SO_4) and Carbonic acid (H_2CO_3) have similar neutralisation equations even though they are different strengths,

i.e. H_2SO_4 + $2NaOH$ $\rightarrow$ Na_2SO_4 + $2H_2O$

H_2CO_3 + $2NaOH$ $\rightarrow$ Na_2CO_3 + $2H_2O$

1 mole of acid requires 2 moles of alkali for neutralisation.

Therefore the same amount of each of these acids requires the same amount of alkali for complete neutralisation.

pH OF SALTS

The **pH of a salt solution** depends on the **strength** of the **acid** and **base** from which it was formed.

> **Acidic salts are salts of strong acids and weak bases**, e.g. ammonium chloride and ammonium nitrate.
>
> **Neutral salts are salts of strong acids and strong bases**, e.g. sodium chloride and potassium nitrate.
>
> **Alkaline salts are salts of weak acids and strong bases**, e.g. potassium carbonate and sodium ethanoate.

Note **Soap** is a **salt** formed between a **fatty acid** and sodium or potassium hydroxide, e.g., **sodium stearate**, $C_{17}H_{35}COONa$.
Soap solutions are **alkaline** as they are the **salts** of **weak acids** and **strong bases**.

EXPLANATION OF pH OF SALTS

The pH of salt solutions can be explained by referring to the following . . .

- **All salts** are **strong electrolytes** and completely ionise in solution.
- The ions of a **weak acid** or **base** when dissolved will set up an **equilibrium** with the ions in water.

Example 1

Consider what happens when an **acid salt** like ammonium chloride dissolves in water.

Ammonium chloride ionises forming lots of NH_4^+ and Cl^- ions.
H^+ and OH^- ions are also present from water.
The ammonium ions set up the following "weak base" equilibrium with the OH^- ions from water. $NH_4^+ (aq) + OH^- (aq) \rightleftharpoons NH_3 (aq) + H_2O$
As OH^- ions are removed the water equilibrium . . .
$H_2O \rightleftharpoons H^+ (aq) + OH^- (aq)$ is affected.
It moves to the RHS to replace the OH^- ions, but this produces an excess of H^+ ions, and the solution is acidic.

Example 2

Consider what happens when an **alkaline salt** like sodium ethanoate dissolves in water.

Sodium ethanoate ionises forming lots of Na^+ and CH_3COO^- ions.
H^+ and OH^- ions are also present from water.
The ethanoate ions set up the following "weak acid" equilibrium with the H^+ ions from water. $CH_3COO^- (aq) + H^+ (aq) \rightleftharpoons CH_3COOH (aq)$
As H^+ ions are removed the water equilibrium . . .
$H_2O \rightleftharpoons H^+ (aq) + OH^- (aq)$ is affected.
It moves to the RHS to replace the H^+ ions but this produces an excess of OH^- ions and the solution is alkaline.

In all solutions of **salts** involving **weak acid** or **base** ions . . .

an equilibrium is established,
the balance of H^+ ions and OH^- ions in water is changed,
water molecules split up to minimise the change,
and the pH is altered.

This is sometimes called **salt hydrolysis**, as the break up of water molecules is caused by the salt dissolving.

REDOX REACTIONS

Common examples of redox reactions are . . .

Metals and acids, displacement reactions, corrosion, electrochemical cells and electrolysis.

This section looks at some of these redox reactions, the chemical changes which occur and associated calculations.

At the end of this section you should be able to . . .   ✔

Explain, with examples, the terms *oxidation* and *reduction*.   ❑
Identify *oxidising* and *reducing agents* in redox processes.   ❑
Write *ion-electron equations* for oxidation and reduction.   ❑
Write *redox equations* for reactions.   ❑
Construct ion-electron equations which include H^+ (aq) and H_2O (*l*).   ❑
Describe how to carry out a *redox titration* and calculation (*ppa*).   ❑
State the quantity of electricity needed to discharge 1 mole of any substance during
    electrolysis.   ❑
State the charge on a mole of electrons.   ❑
Describe how to find the quantity of electricity needed to produce a mole of an element
    during electrolysis (*ppa*).   ❑
Calculate the mass or volume of an element discharged, during an electrolysis, from the
    quantity of electricity passed and vice-versa.   ❑

WORD LIST

The following words are introduced or used in this topic. You should be able to define, use and give examples of them where appropriate.

amps	ion-electron equation	reducing agent
coulombs	oxidation	reduction
electrolysis	oxidising agent	spectator ion
electrolyte	redox reaction	titration

If you are not familiar with the meaning of any of these words, you should refer to the Glossary, where these words are defined.

REDOX REACTIONS

Redox reactions involve the **transfer of electrons** between species.

Oxidation	Reduction
Is	Is
Loss of electrons	Gain of electrons

Reducing agents are mainly metals and negative ions and they lose electrons, e.g.

Zn (s) $\rightarrow$ Zn^{2+} (aq) + 2e
$2I^-$ (aq) $\rightarrow$ I_2 (s) + 2e

Reducing agents are **oxidised**.

Oxidising agents are mainly non-metals and positive ions and they gain electrons, e.g.

Cl_2 (g) + 2e $\rightarrow$ $2Cl^-$ (aq)
Cu^{2+} (aq) + 2e $\rightarrow$ Cu (s)

Oxidising agents are **reduced**.

ION-ELECTRON AND REDOX EQUATIONS

Ion-electron equations show where the electrons are lost and gained in a **redox reaction**.

Examples can be found in *"The electrochemical series"* in the data book. Note that the reactions and the equations are reversible and are written . . .

from left to right   **— reduction →**
and from right to left   **← oxidation —**

Adding the two **ion-electron equations** together after balancing and cancelling out the electrons gives the **Redox equation**, which shows the overall change.

Example 1

In the reaction between magnesium and hydrochloric acid . . .
$$Mg \text{ (s)} + 2H^+ Cl^- \text{ (aq)} \rightarrow Mg^{2+} (Cl^-)_2 \text{ (aq)} + H_2 \text{ (g)}$$

The **ion-electron equations** are . . .

Oxidation $Mg(s) \qquad\qquad \rightarrow Mg^{2+} \text{ (aq)} + 2e$
Reduction $2H^+ \text{ (aq)} + 2e \rightarrow H_2 \text{ (g)}$

These can be combined, to give the **redox equation**.

$$\boxed{Mg \text{ (s)} + 2H^+ \text{ (aq)} \rightarrow Mg^{2+} \text{ (aq)} + H_2 \text{ (g)}}$$

This is the same as the overall reaction, with the **spectator ions** (Cl^-) missing.

Example 2

Magnesium metal can be used to reduce iron (III) ions to iron.

The **ion-electron equations** are . . .

Oxidation $Mg \text{ (s)} \qquad\qquad \rightarrow Mg^{2+} \text{ (aq)} + 2e$
Reduction $Fe^{3+} \text{ (aq)} + 3e \rightarrow Fe \text{ (s)}$

Balance the electrons by multiplying the *oxidation* ×3 and the *reduction* ×2, add together for the **redox equation**.

$$\boxed{3\, Mg \text{ (s)} + 2\, Fe^{3+} \text{ (aq)} \rightarrow Mg^{2+} \text{ (aq)} + 2Fe \text{ (s)}}$$

Example 3

Potassium iodide solution reduces iron(III) chloride solution to form iron(II) ions and iodine.

The **ion-electron equations** are . . .

Oxidation $2I^- \text{ (aq)} \qquad \rightarrow I_2 \text{ (aq)} + 2e$
Reduction $Fe^{3+} \text{ (aq)} + e \rightarrow Fe^{2+} \text{ (aq)}$

Balance the electrons by multiplying the *reduction* ×2, then add together for the **redox equation**.

$$\boxed{2I^- \text{ (aq)} + 2Fe^{3+} \text{ (aq)} \rightarrow I_2 \text{ (aq)} + Fe^{2+} \text{ (aq)}}$$

The K^+ and Cl^- are spectator ions.

COMPLEX ION-ELECTRON EQUATIONS

The data book includes some complex **ion-electron equations** involving H^+ (aq) and H_2O, e.g.
$$MnO_4^- + 8H^+ (aq) + 6e^- \rightarrow Mn^{2+} (aq) + 4H_2O$$
Complex ion-electron equations can sometimes be worked out as shown below.

Example

What is the ion-electron equation for the reduction of dichromate ions to chromium (III) ions?

The basic change is
$$Cr_2O_7^{2-} (aq) \rightarrow Cr^{3+} (aq)$$
First balance the number of chromium atoms
$$Cr_2O_7^{2-} (aq) \rightarrow 2Cr^{3+} (aq)$$
Then balance the oxygen atoms by adding water to RHS
$$Cr_2O_7^{2-} (aq) \rightarrow 2Cr^{3+} (aq) + 7H_2O(l)$$
Now balance the hydrogen atoms by adding H^+ (aq) ions to LHS
$$Cr_2O_7^{2-} (aq) + 14H^+ (aq) \rightarrow 2Cr^{3+} (aq) + 7H_2O(l)$$
Finally count up the charges on each side and add electrons to balance the equation electrically.
$$\mathbf{Cr_2O_7^{2-} (aq) + 14H^+ (aq) + 6e \rightarrow 2Cr^{3+} (aq) + 7H_2O(l)}$$

LHS charge = (2−) + (14+) + (6−)   RHS charge = (2 × 3+)
= 6+   = 6+

Note   The reduction of $\mathbf{Cr_2O_7^{2-}}$ (aq) and $\mathbf{MnO_4^-}$ (aq) requires the presence of $\mathbf{H^+}$ **(aq)**. This explains why solutions of these ions have to be **acidified** before they can act as **oxidising agents**.

REDOX TITRATIONS

The amount of oxidising or reducing agent present can be calculated from the results of a titration by using . . .

●   The **balanced redox equation** to find the mole ratios of reactants.

● $\mathbf{N_m = C . V}$ Where N_m = number of moles
                             C = concentration (mol l^{-1})
                  and V = volume (l)
to find the number of moles in a given volume of solution.

Investigating a redox titration

Aim

To determine the mass of vitamin ($C_6H_8O_6$) in a tablet by redox titration, using a solution of iodine of known concentration, with starch as an indicator.

Method

A vitamin C tablet is dissolved in deionised water and transferred to a 250 cm^3 volumetric flask, which is made up to the mark.

A titration is carried out using the apparatus shown opposite.

The iodine solution (0·02 mol l^{-1}) is slowly added to 25 cm^3 samples of the vitamin C solution. Starch is added as an indicator.

As the iodine is added the blue/black colour, formed with the starch, initially disappears quickly. The end point of the reaction is found when the blue/black colour just remains.

Results

Titration		Volume
Rough titre	=	19·6 cm^3
2nd titre	=	19·2 cm^3
3rd titre	=	19·0 cm^3
Average titre	=	19·1 cm^3

Note Rough titre ignored when calculating the average.

∴   19·1 cm^3 0·02 mol l^{-1} iodine is required to react completely with 25 cm^3 of the vitamin C solution.

Calculations

The number of moles of iodine in the titre can be calculated

$$Nm = C \times V$$
$$Nm = 0·02 \times 0·0191$$
$$= 3·82 \times 10^{-4} \, mol$$

The balanced redox equation for the reaction is . . .

$$C_6H_8O_6 \ + \ I_2 \ \rightarrow \ C_6H_6O_6 \ + \ 2H^+ \ + \ 2I^-$$

∴   1 mole I_2 ⇔ 1 mole $C_6H_8O_6$

∴ $3·82 \times 10^{-4}$ mol I_2 ⇔ $3·82 \times 10^{-4}$ mol $C_6H_8O_6$

Now the vitamin C tablet was dissolved in 250 cm^3

$\therefore$ If 25 cm^3 of solution $\Leftrightarrow$ 3.82×10^{-4} mol $C_6H_8O_6$

250 cm^3 of solution $\Leftrightarrow$ $\dfrac{250}{25} \times 3.82 \times 10^{-4}$ mol $C_6H_8O_6$

$= 3.82 \times 10^{-3}$ mol $C_6H_8O_6$

Now 1 mole of vitamin C ($C_6H_8O_6$) $=$ 176 g
$\therefore$ 3.82×10^{-3} mole $C_6H_8O_6$ $= 3.82 \times 10^{-3} \times 176$

$\therefore$ **Mass of vitamin C in one tablet = 0.672 g**

ELECTROLYSIS AND THE MOLE

Electrolysis involves the passage of electricity through an **electrolyte solution**.

This causes a **redox reaction** to occur with **ions discharged** at each electrode.

The quantity of electricity passed is measured in **coulombs** (symbol C) and depends on the current and the length of time it is passed.

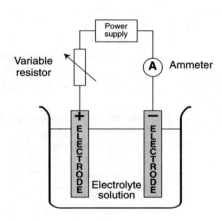

As 1C $\Leftrightarrow$ 1 amp passed for 1 sec,
i.e.

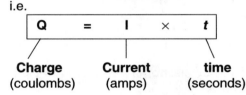

| Q | = | I | × | t |

Charge **Current** **time**
(coulombs) (amps) (seconds)

Michael Faraday found that **1 mole** of any substance was **discharged** by . . .

$$n \times 96\,500\ C$$

where n was an integer and was related to the ion electron equation, e.g.

1 mole of silver discharged by . . .
$\quad\quad$ Ag^+ (aq) $+$ e $\rightarrow$ Ag (s) requires $1 \times 96\,500$ C
1 mole of Copper discharged by . . .
$\quad\quad$ Cu^{2+} (aq) $+$ 2e $\rightarrow$ Cu (s) requires $2 \times 96\,500$ C
1 mole of oxygen discharged by . . .
$\quad\quad$ $4OH^-$ (aq) $\rightarrow$ O_2(g) $+$ H_2O(l) $+$ 4e requires $4 \times 96\,500$ C

Therefore n is the number of **moles of electrons** lost or gained to discharge **1 mole** of the substance and **96 500 C**, called **1 Faraday (F)**, must be the total charge of **1 mole of electrons**.

To carry out calculations involving electrolysis, the following facts should be used.

1. During an electrolysis **one mole** of an element is discharged when $n \times$ **96 500 coulombs** of charge is passed.

2. The charge (in coulombs) passed is found by $Q = I \times t$.

Example 1

If a current of 0·5 amps was passed through a solution of silver(I)nitrate for 30 minutes, what mass of silver would be deposited at the negative electrode?

During the electrolysis . . .
$$Q = I \times t$$
$$= 0.5 \times 30 \times 60$$
$$= 900 \text{ C of electric charge passed}$$

The ion-electron equation is $Ag^+ (aq) + e \rightarrow Ag (s)$

∴   1 mole of silver is discharged by 96 500 C (1 Faraday) and 1 mole of silver $\Leftrightarrow$ 108 g

∴   96 500 C $\Leftrightarrow$ 108 g silver

∴   1 C $\Leftrightarrow \dfrac{108}{96\,500}$ g

∴   900 C $\Leftrightarrow \dfrac{108}{96\,500} \times 900$

$$= \textbf{1g of Ag}$$

Example 2

Aluminium is extracted from the molten aluminium oxide ore by electrolysis. How long would it take to extract 54 kg of aluminium by using a current of 4000 A?

The ion-electron equation is $Al^{3+} + 3e \rightarrow Al$

∴   1 mole of aluminium is discharged by $3 \times 96\,500$ C and 1 mole of aluminium $\Leftrightarrow$ 27 g
∴   27g of Al $\Leftrightarrow 3 \times 96\,500$ C

∴   1g of Al $\Leftrightarrow 3 \times \dfrac{96\,500}{27}$

∴   54 000g (54kg) $\Leftrightarrow 3 \times \dfrac{96\,500}{27} \times 54\,000$

$$= 5.79 \times 10^8 \text{ C}$$

Since $Q = I \times t$

then $t = \dfrac{Q}{I}$

∴   The time needed to discharge 54 kg $= \dfrac{5.79 \times 10^8}{4000}$

$$= \textbf{1·4475} \times \textbf{10}^\textbf{5} \textbf{ sec}$$

Investigating quantitative electrolysis

Aim

To find the quantity of electricity required to discharge a mole of hydrogen gas by the electrolysis of a sulphuric acid solution.

Method

Set up the circuit shown opposite.

Pass a measured current through the sulphuric acid solution for a fixed time. Use the variable resistor to control the current.

Switch off the current and note the time taken, then measure the volume of hydrogen gas produced.

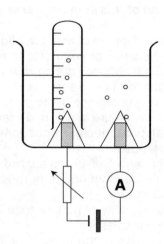

Results

Current passed	= 0·5 amps	molar gas volume = 24·1 litres mol^{-1}
Time passed	= 15 minutes	
Volume of gas	= 59 cm^3	

Calculations

Now $Q = I \times t$

$$= 0{\cdot}5 \times 15 \times 60$$

$$= 450 \text{ C}$$

∴ 59 cm^3 of hydrogen is discharged by 450 C

∴ 59 cm^3 of hydrogen $\Leftrightarrow$ 450 C

∴ 1 cm^3 of hydrogen $\Leftrightarrow \dfrac{450}{59}$ C

∴ 24 100 cm^3 (1 mole) $\Leftrightarrow 24\,100 \times \dfrac{450}{59}$

$$= 183\,814 \text{ C}$$

∴ **1 mole of hydrogen is discharged by 183 814 C.**

RADIOISOTOPES

This section introduces the chemistry of **radioisotopes** and **radioactivity**. The main areas covered include nuclear decay, types of radiation, nuclear equations, half-life and the uses of radioisotopes.

At the end of this section you should be able to . . .   ✔

Describe the nature of an atom and the sub-atomic particles.   ❐
Explain the terms *atomic number*, *mass number* and *isotopes*.   ❐
Explain what happens during *radioactive decay*.   ❐
Explain the term *radioisotopes*.   ❐
Explain the importance of the proton/neutron balance in an atom.   ❐
Describe the nature of α, β and γ radiation.   ❐
Write balanced nuclear equations which include neutrons, protons, α-particles and
      β-particles.   ❐
Define the term *half-life*, as applied to radioisotopes.   ❐
Explain the random nature of radiation and its independence of chemical and physical
      conditions.   ❐
Calculate quantity of radioisotope, half-life or time elapsed given the value of the other
      two variables.   ❐
Give examples of the uses of radioisotopes in medicine, industry, scientific research,
      carbon dating and energy production.   ❐
Explain the differences between *nuclear fusion* and *nuclear fission*.   ❐
Explain the choice of a particular radioisotope for a job in terms of the type of radiation, its
      intensity and its half-life.   ❐
Describe some of the problems of using radioisotopes.   ❐
Compare nuclear and fossil fuels in terms of safety, pollution and use of finite
      resources.   ❐
Explain the origin of all the naturally occurring elements.   ❐

WORD LIST

The following words are introduced or used in this topic. You should be able to define, use and give examples of them where appropriate.

alpha radiation	element	nuclear fission
atom	gamma radiation	nuclear fusion
atomic number	half-life	nuclear power
beta radiation	isotopes	nucleus
chain reaction	mass number	proton
decay	neutron	radioisotopes
electron	nuclear equation	sub-atomic particle

If you are not familiar with the meaning of any of these words, you should refer to the Glossary, where these words are defined.

ATOMS AND ATOMIC STRUCTURE

All the substances in the universe, elements, compounds and mixtures, are made up of tiny particles called **atoms**.

Atoms are the building blocks of **matter**.

All atoms have a similar **structure** . . .

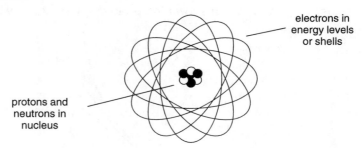

electrons in energy levels or shells

protons and neutrons in nucleus

Remember the properties of the **sub-atomic particles**.

Particle	Charge	Relative Mass
Proton	positive	1
Neutron	neutral	1
Electron	negative	1/1840

Describing an atom

Along with the elements **symbol**, atoms are described by two numbers . . .

atomic number = number of protons
mass number = number of protons + neutrons

i.e.

Mass No.
Symbol
Atomic No.

Atoms are usually electrically neutral as . . .
    number of protons = number of electrons

Hydrogen has the simplest atoms with 1 proton, 1 electron and 0 neutrons — $^{1}_{1}H$

Uranium atoms have 92 protons, 92 electrons and 143 neutrons — $^{235}_{92}U$

Isotopes are atoms which have
the **same atomic number**
but **different mass numbers**.
They are atoms of the same element
which have different numbers of neutrons
in their nuclei.

e.g. Isotopes of chlorine

$^{35}_{17}Cl$ and $^{37}_{17}Cl$

Isotopes are atoms of the same element. They may have different masses but they are chemically identical as the number and arrangement of electrons are the same.

RADIOACTIVITY

Radioactivity involves the break-up of **unstable nuclei**, with the emission of **radiation** and the **release of energy**. During radioactive decay, the unstable nuclei are changed into more stable nuclei.

The stability of a nuclei depends on the **proton/neutron ratio** or balance.

Consider the graph, which shows the proton/neutron ratios which produce stable and unstable atoms.

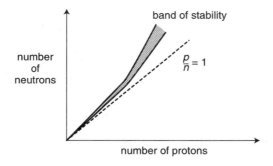

Note that all isotopes of elements with atomic numbers greater than 83 are unstable and therefore radioactive.

It is possible to make radioactive isotopes called **radioisotopes** of almost any element. This can be done by bombarding the nuclei of stable isotopes with neutrons or other sub-atomic particles to change their make-up.

TYPES OF RADIATION

There are three main types of **radiation**, with different properties . . .

Type of radiation	Nature	Symbol	Mass	Charge	Penetration (i.e. stopped by)
alpha (α)	helium nucleus	$^{4}_{2}\text{He}$	4	2+	few cm of air
beta (β)	electron	$^{0}_{-1}\text{e}$	0	1–	thin metal foil
gamma (γ)	e.m.r	γ	0	0	few cm of lead

The break-up of an **unstable nuclei** may result in the emission of one or more of these types of radiation.

The emission of radiation from an atom will change its nature. Here are examples of **nuclear equations**, showing the products of nuclear decay. In nuclear equations, the sum of the **atomic and mass numbers** on each side of the equation should **balance**.

Example 1   alpha emission $^{232}_{90}\text{Th} \rightarrow {}^{228}_{88}\text{Ra} + {}^{4}_{2}\text{He}$

Example 2   beta emission $^{14}_{6}\text{C} \rightarrow {}^{14}_{7}\text{N} + {}^{0}_{-1}\text{e}$

The emission of gamma radiation, a form of electromagnetic radiation like light or X-rays, does not change the nature of the atom.

All radioisotopes continue to **decay** (give off radiation) until they form **a stable isotope**.

OTHER NUCLEAR REACTIONS

Nuclear reactions can also be brought about by bombarding the nuclei of atoms with small particles.

Example 3 $^{14}_{7}\text{N} + {}^{4}_{2}\text{He} \rightarrow {}^{17}_{8}\text{O} + {}^{1}_{1}\text{H}$

Example 4 $^{10}_{5}\text{B} + {}^{1}_{0}\text{n} \rightarrow {}^{3}_{1}\text{H} + 2{}^{4}_{2}\text{He}$

Other nuclear reactions can involve different decay products.

Example 5 $^{4}_{2}\text{He} + {}^{14}_{7}\text{N} \rightarrow {}^{2}_{1}\text{H} + {}^{16}_{8}\text{O}$

Example 6 $^{7}_{3}\text{Li} \rightarrow {}^{3}_{1}\text{H} + {}^{4}_{2}\text{He}$

Remember   The sum of the atomic numbers and mass numbers on each side of a nuclear equation must always balance.

RATE OF RADIOACTIVE DECAY

The **disintegration** or **decay** of an unstable nuclei is a random event and is independent of chemical or physical conditions.

The **activity**, amount of radiation given off, from any particular radioisotope will only depend on the isotope's stability and the number of unstable nuclei present.

Note   The **activity** will be greater the more unstable the nuclei and the greater the number of unstable nuclei present.

Stability or **rate of decay** of a radioisotope is measured by its **half-life**.

The **half-life** of a **radioisotope** is the time taken for the **number** of unstable nuclei present and the sample's **activity** to fall by half.

Consider the typical radioactive decay graph shown below.

The activity decreases with time as the radioisotope decays and the number of unstable nuclei present decreases.

The half-life is 10 minutes.

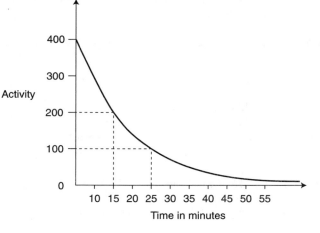

The half-life can be calculated from the graph.

The half-life of a particular radioisotope is constant but can vary for different radioisotopes from a millisecond to thousands of years.

The shorter the half-life the more unstable the nuclei of the radioisotope.

RADIOACTIVITY CALCULATIONS

Calculations can involve half-life, quantity, time elapsed and activity.

Example 1

The mass of a radioisotope falls from 1·6 g to 0·1 g in 2 hours. What is the half-life of this radioisotope?

	Original mass of radioisotope	= 1·6 g
∴	mass of radioisotope after 1 half-life	= 0·8 g
∴	mass of radioisotope after 2 half-lives	= 0·4 g
∴	mass of radioisotope after 3 half-lives	= 0·2 g
∴	mass of radioisotope after 4 half-lives	= 0·1 g

∴   4 half-lives   =   2 hours (120 minutes)

∴   **Half-life of radioisotope** $= \dfrac{120}{4}$

$= $ **30 minutes**

Example 2

If a 1 g sample of a radioisotope with a half-life of 3 days has an activity of 32 counts sec^{-1}, how long would it take for the activity of a 2 g sample to fall to 8 counts sec^{-1}?

Original activity of 1g sample = 32 counts sec^{-1}
∴ Original activity of 2g sample = 64 counts sec^{-1}

∴ Activity after 1 half-life   = 32 counts sec^{-1}
∴ Activity after 2 half-lives = 16 counts sec^{-1}
∴ Activity after 3 half-lives = 8 counts sec^{-1}

Now 1 half-life = 3 days
∴ 3 half-lives   = 3×3 = 9 days

∴ **Time to fall to 8 counts sec^{-1} = 9 days**

USES OF RADIOISOTOPES

A variety of **radioisotopes** are used to our benefit in **medicine, industry, scientific research** and **energy production**. Different radioisotopes are needed for each job as the type of radiation emitted and the half-life of the sample are important to the application.

In **medicine**, radioisotopes are used to kill cancer cells. Here the penetrating gamma and beta radiations are required. Radioisotopes can be used as "tracers", and injected into the body to investigate internal organs. These isotopes should have a short half-life so that they are in the body for as little time as possible.

In **industry**, radioisotopes are used in measuring devices to gauge the thickness of sheet materials, like paper or steel. These radioisotopes would have a long half-life, so they last, and use either gamma or beta radiation depending on the penetrating power required.

In **scientific research**, radioisotopes are used in the investigation of reaction mechanisms. where radioactive "labelled" atoms can be detected in one of the products.

Radiocarbon dating uses the natural radioisotope of carbon, ^{14}C, which is formed in the upper atmosphere.

Plants take in carbon dioxide, from the atmosphere, during **photosynthesis** and animals eat plants. So all living things contain a constant level of radioactive carbon during their life. On death, however, the amount of radioactivity starts to decrease and knowing the half-life of ^{14}C is 5700 years, scientists can estimate the age of a once living specimen by measuring the amount of radioactive carbon which is left. The method is, however, inaccurate for samples older than 50 000 years as the radiation levels are too low.

FISSION AND NUCLEAR ENERGY

Nuclear power stations, which produce 50% of Scotland's electricity, can use isotopes of uranium or plutonium as their fuel.

The uranium-235 is bombarded with neutrons, the atoms split and release **energy**. This is called **nuclear fission**, e.g.

$$^{235}_{92}U + {}^{1}_{0}n \rightarrow {}^{90}_{38}Sr + {}^{143}_{54}Xe + 3{}^{1}_{0}n$$

The **fission** produces more than one neutron which can initiate the splitting of other atoms and so a **chain reaction** can build up producing large amounts of **energy**.

In **nuclear power stations**, where the chain reaction is controlled by using graphite rods to absorb the neutrons, the fission reaction is used to produce **electricity**.

The uncontrolled chain reaction can be used in **atomic bombs** with devastating results.

Advantages of nuclear fuels over coal and oil in power stations . . .
> Resources of nuclear fuels will last longer than fossil fuels.
> Nuclear power stations do not produce CO_2 or SO_2, which contribute to the "greenhouse effect" and "acid rain".

Disadvantages of nuclear power are . . .
> The production of large amounts of dangerous radioactive waste, which has to be stored for a long time.
> The possibility of leaks of radioactive material into the environment.
> The high costs of setting up and decommissioning nuclear plants.

FUSION AND NUCLEAR ENERGY

In **nuclear fusion**, two small nuclei combine or **fuse** together to form a larger nucleus with the release of enormous amounts of **energy**, e.g.

$$^{2}_{1}H + {}^{3}_{1}H \rightarrow {}^{4}_{2}He + {}^{1}_{0}n$$

Nuclear fusion is potentially the answer to the world's energy needs as there is a plentiful supply of small nuclei and the fusion reaction creates no dangerous waste problems. However, scientists have not yet been able to find a way of controlling the power of nuclear fusion, the main difficulty being the temperature of 200 million °C which is required to initiate the reaction.

RADIATION HAZARDS

The use of radioisotopes in medicine, fallout from testing atomic bombs, "leaks" from nuclear power plants and other sources of **radioactivity** can be dangerous, as any exposure to radioactivity can be harmful to living things.

High levels of radiation can cause sickness, diarrhoea, burns and death. Even small doses of radiation can promote cell damage, cancers and genetic changes.

Great care is therefore needed in the control and use of all types of radioisotopes and radiation.

ELEMENTS AND THE STARS

The **"big bang theory"** suggests that our universe was created by a massive **explosion** which produced a mixture of **hydrogen** and **helium** gas.

A young star, like our sun, is mainly made up of this **hydrogen** and **helium** and produces its energy by **nuclear fusion**. During the lifetime of a star, **nuclear fusion** can produce atoms of elements as heavy as iron. While the heaviest elements are only formed in special conditions, as in a "super nova", the violent death of a star.

This means that **all atoms** of naturally occurring **elements** which are found on earth, including those in our bodies, **originated** in a **star**.

GLOSSARY

Check your understanding of the following words and terms which are used in the Higher Chemistry course.

acid	A substance which produces excess H^+ ions in solution.
acid rain	Rain which has a lower pH than normal.
activated complex	Short lived intermediate between reactants and products.
activation energy	Minimum energy needed by reactant molecules.
active sites	Areas on a catalyst which can adsorb reacting molecules.
addition polymer	Long chain molecule made by joining monomers which contain a $C = C$ double bond.
addition reaction	Reaction involving the breaking of a $C = C$ double bond or a $C \equiv C$ triple bond.
adsorbed	Held by weak forces of attractions (on the surface of a catalyst).
alcohol	Any group of organic compounds containing an —OH hydroxyl group.
aldehyde	Any organic compound containing a $C = O$ carbonyl group on the end carbon atom.
alkali	Solution containing excess OH^- ions.
alkali metal	Element in group 1 of the Periodic Table.
alkanal	Straight chain organic series containing a $C = O$ carbonyl group on the end carbon atom.
alkane	Straight chain hydrocarbon series containing only single bonds.
alkanoic acid	Straight chain organic series containing a — COOH carboxyl group.
alkanol	Straight chain organic series containing a — OH hydroxyl group.
alkanone	Straight chain organic series containing a $C = O$ carbonyl group on a middle carbon atom.
alkene	Straight chain organic series containing a $C = C$ double bond group.
alkynes	Straight chain organic series containing a $C \equiv C$ triple bond group.
alpha radiation	Radioactive decay product consisting of helium nuclei.
amide link	Linking group formed between amino group and carboxyl group.
amine	Organic series containing an $-NH_2$ amino group.
amino acid	Organic series containing an amino group and a carboxyl group.
amino group	Functional group — NH_2.
amp	Unit of electric current.
anaerobic	Occurring without oxygen or air being present.
aromatic	Organic compound containing the benzene ring.
atactic polymer	Polymer chain with side groups arranged randomly.
atom	Smallest particle of matter which can take part in a chemical reaction.
atomic number	Number of protons in an atom.
atomic volume	Size of atom, related to the number of electron shells and the nuclear charge.
auto-ignition	Fuel self-igniting without a spark.
Avogadro's constant	The number of formula units in a mole of a substance $= 6 \cdot 02 \times 10^{23}$ mol^{-1}.

base	Substance which can combine with an acid to form a salt.
batch process	Raw materials are mixed in a vessel and the product separated when the reaction is completed.
Benedict's solution	Test for aldehyde, colour change blue to orange.
benzene	Hydrocarbon (C_6H_6) which is formed by reforming naphtha and is the basis of all aromatic compounds.
beta radiation	Radioactive decay product consisting of electrons.
biodegradable	Material which can be broken down in nature.
biogas	Fuel, mainly made up of methane, produced by the anaerobic fermentation of biomass.
biomass	Mixture of once living material, mainly from plants, e.g. compost.
Biopol	A biodegradable polyester polymer.
bitumen	Heaviest "tar" fraction from crude oil.
blended	Made by mixing different components.
capital costs	Cost involved in setting up a manufacturing process.
carbohydrate	Compound of carbon, hydrogen and oxygen formed in plants by photosynthesis.
carbonyl group	Functional group $C = O$.
carboxyl group	Functional group — COOH.
carboxylic acid	Any organic compound containing a — COOH carboxyl group.
catalyst	Substance which speeds up a chemical reaction without being used up.
catalyst poisoning	Surface of catalyst being covered with another substance so it no longer works.
catalytic cracking	Breaking up long chain hydrocarbons using a catalyst.
chain reaction	A sequence of reactions which keep themselves going.
chlorofluorocarbon	Haloalkane used as refrigerant and solvent, partly responsible for damage to "ozone layer".
chromatography	Technique used to separate and identify mixtures.
collision geometry	The angle at which molecules must collide to react.
collision theory	Reaction will only occur if the molecules collide with sufficient energy.
combustion	Burning, combining with oxygen with the release of energy.
compound	A substance which contains atoms of different elements joined together.
concentration	The number of moles of solute in one litre of solution.
condensation polymer	Long chain molecule formed by a condensation reaction between monomers with two functional groups.
condensation reaction	Reaction which involves the elimination of water from between two molecules.
continuous process	Raw materials are fed in at one end of the plant and the products are removed as they are formed.
coulomb	Unit of electric charge, 1 amp per second.
covalent bonding	Bond formed between non-metals by the equal sharing of electrons.
cross-link	Bonding between polymer chains forming a 3D structure.
crude oil	Complex mixture of hydrocarbons formed over millions of years from tiny, dead, sea creatures.
cycloalkane	Series of hydrocarbons with atoms formed in a ring.
decay	Break-up of an unstable nucleus.

dehydration	The removal of water from a compound.
denatured	Enzyme changes shape and no longer works.
diamond	Form of carbon with 4 bonds and tetrahedral structure.
diatomic molecule	Two atom molecule.
diesel	Fuel formed by blending gas oil fractions.
dipole	Separation of charge and charged ends.
distillation	Separating liquids by using their different boiling points.
dynamic equilibrium	Forward and back reactions continue at the same rate.
electrolysis	The passage of electricity through a solution or melt containing ions.
electrolyte	A substance which conducts as it contains mobile ions.
electron	Negatively charged sub-atomic particle.
electron arrangement	Arrangement of electrons, in shells or energy levels around the nucleus.
electronegativity	A measure of an atom's attraction for bonded electrons.
electrostatic forces	Forces of attraction between opposite charges.
element	A substance which only contains atoms with the same atomic number.
endothermic	Reaction which takes in heat energy ΔH +ve.
enthalpy change	Change in heat content from reactants to products.
enthalpy of combustion	Heat energy given out when 1 mole of a substance burns completely in excess oxygen.
enthalpy of formation	Heat energy given out or taken in when 1 mole of a substance is formed from its elements in their normal states.
enthalpy of neutralisation	Heat energy given out when 1 mole of water is formed by neutralisation of acid by alkali.
enthalpy of solution	Heat energy given out or taken in when 1 mole of a substance dissolves in excess water.
enzyme	Protein molecule which acts as a biological catalyst.
equilibrium	Concentrations of reactants and products remain constant as forward and back reactions continue at the same rate.
essential amino acid	Amino acid which cannot be synthesised in the body and must be present in our diet.
ester	Compound formed by a condensation reaction between an alcohol and a carboxylic acid.
esterification	Condensation reaction between an alcohol and a carboxylic acid.
excess reactants	Substances which are not completely used up in a chemical reaction.
exothermic	Reaction which gives out heat ΔH −ve.
fats	Energy store in animals, a solid ester of glycerol and a long chain carboxylic acid.
fatty acid	Long chain carboxylic acid between C_4 to C_{24}.
feedstock	A substance from which other chemicals can be extracted or synthesised.
fermentation	The action of microbes or enzymes on organic material.
fibrous protein	Protein chains formed into long, thin structures.
finite	Something which will eventually run out.
fixed costs	Manufacturing costs which are independent of the level of production.

flammability	How easily a substance catches fire.
formula unit	Atoms, molecules or ions which make up the formula of a substance, used in calculations.
fractional distillation	Distillation of complex mixture into fractions of compounds with similar boiling points.
fuel	Something which is a source of energy.
fullerenes	Form of carbon with spherical molecules.
functional group	Group of atoms which give a molecule its distinctive chemical properties.
gamma radiation	High energy electromagnetic radiation which often accompanies radioactive decay.
gas oil	Fractions from crude oil used to make diesel fuel.
gasoline	Fractions from crude oil used to make petrol.
globular protein	Protein chains folded into a spherical shape.
glycerol	Propan-1,2,3-triol, product of hydrolysis of a fat.
graphite	Form of carbon with three bonds and layer structure.
greenhouse effect	The trapping of the sun's energy by gases in the atmosphere, e.g. carbon dioxide.
group	Vertical column of elements, in the Periodic Table, with similar chemical properties.
Haber Process	Manufacture of ammonia from nitrogen and hydrogen gas using an iron catalyst.
half-life	Time taken for the number of radioactive nuclei and their activity to fall by half.
haloalkanes	Alkane with one or more hydrogen atoms substituted by a halogen atom.
halogen	Element in group 7 in the Periodic Table.
hardening	Converting oils into fats by the addition of hydrogen.
Hess's Law	The overall enthalpy change is independent of the route taken.
heterogeneous catalyst	A catalyst which is in a different state from the reactants.
homogeneous catalyst	A catalyst which is in the same state as the reactants.
homologous series	Series of compounds with similar chemical properties and fit a general formula, e.g. alkanes.
hydration	The addition of water to a compound.
hydrocarbon	Compound of carbon and hydrogen atoms only, e.g. methane.
hydrogenation	The addition of hydrogen to a compound.
hydrogen bonds	Forces of attraction between the oppositely charged ends of very polar molecules where hydrogen is bonded to nitrogen, oxygen or fluorine.
hydrolysis reaction	The splitting up of a molecule by addition of water.
hydroxyl group	Functional group — OH.
intermolecular bonding	Any force of attraction between molecules.
ion-electron equation	Equation showing the loss or gain of electrons by an atom or ion.
ionic bonding	Bond formed by the loss and gain of electrons.
ionic lattice	Regular array of ions held together by the attraction of opposite charges.
ionic product of water	Product of $[H^+] \times [OH^-] = 10^{-14}$ mol^2 l^{-2} which is constant for all solutions in water.

ionisation enthalpy   Energy needed to remove a mole of electrons from a mole of atoms in the gaseous state.

isomer   Compounds with the same molecular formula but different structural formula.

isotactic polymer   Polymer with all side groups arranged on the same side of the polymer chain.

isotopes   Atoms with the same atomic number but different mass numbers.

kerosine   Fraction from crude oil used to make paraffin.

ketone   Any organic compound containing a $C = O$ carbonyl group on a middle carbon atom.

Kevlar   A strong and light aromatic polyamide polymer.

kilojoules   Units of energy, 1 kJ = 1000 J.

kinetic energy   Movement energy of particles.

knocking   Uneven engine running due to auto-ignition.

lattice structure   Any regular arrangement of atoms or ions.

leaded petrol   Petrol with lead compound additive to increase octane number.

mass number   Number of protons and neutrons in an atom.

metallic bonding   Bonds formed between metal atoms by freely moving outer electrons.

metallic lattice   Regular array of metal atoms held together by electrostatic forces.

molar gas volume   Volume, in litres, occupied by a mole of any gas at a set temperature and pressure (units $/mol^{-1}$).

mole   The formula mass of a substance in grams.

molecular structure   Small discrete groups of atoms held together by covalent bonds.

monatomic   Made up of single unbonded atoms, e.g. helium.

monomer   Units which are joined together to make polymers.

naphtha   Light fraction from crude oil C_5 to C_{10} used as a feedstock for many different chemicals.

natural gas   Fuel found along with oil, mainly made of methane.

network structure   Large regular arrangement of atoms bonded together.

neutralisation   When a base cancels out an acid forming a salt.

neutron   Neutral sub-atomic particle.

noble gas   Element in Group 8 of the Periodic Table.

non-polar molecule   Molecule without charged ends.

non-polar solvent   Solvent made up of molecules without charged ends.

nuclear equation   Radioactive decay equation showing the mass numbers and atomic numbers of the particles.

nuclear fission   The splitting of large atoms to form smaller atoms.

nuclear fusion   The combining of two small atoms to make a larger atom.

nuclear power   Production of energy by nuclear fission.

nucleus   Centre of atom containing protons and neutrons.

nylon   Strong synthetic polyamide polymer.

octane number   Rating of fuel describing how evenly it burns.

oils   Energy store in plants and animals, a liquid ester of glycerol and a long chain carboxylic acid.

organic   Carbon containing compounds based on molecules originating from living things.

oxidation	The loss of electrons by an atom or ion.
oxidation (organic)	The gain of oxygen or the loss of hydrogen by a molecule.
oxidising agent	Substance which takes electrons away from an atom or ion and is reduced itself.
oxygenates	Compounds containing oxygen added to petrol to raise its octane rating.
peptide link	Linking group formed between amino group and carboxyl group.
period	Horizontal row of elements in the Periodic Table.
Periodic Table	Classification of the elements in increasing atomic number into groups and periods.
pH scale	Scale of acid/alkaline properties, related to the H^+ ion concentration of a solution.
phenyl group	Benzene substituted group, — C_6H_5.
photochemical reactions	Reactions which are initiated by light energy.
photoconducting	Conducts electricity better in light.
photodegradable polymers	Polymers that are broken down by light.
polar molecule	Molecule with charged ends due to uneven distribution of charge.
polar solvent	Solvent containing molecules which have charged ends.
polar-covalent bonding	Bond formed between atoms by the unequal sharing of electrons.
polar-polar attractions	Forces of attraction between the oppositely charged ends of polar molecules.
polyamide	or **polypeptide**. A condensation polymer formed from a diamine and a diacid with amide links.
polyester	Polymer formed by condensation of a diol with a diacid.
polyester fibre	Long chain polyester which forms fibres suitable for textile manufacture.
polyester resin	Polyester formed with cross-links which has a rigid structure.
Polyethanol	Addition polymer which is soluble in water.
Polyethene	Addition polymer formed from ethene.
polyethyne	Addition polymer with many C = C double bonds.
Polymer	Long chain molecule made up of repeating units.
polypeptide	or **polyamide**. A condensation polymer formed from a diamine and a diacid with peptide links.
polypropene	Addition polymer formed from propene.
poly vinyl carbazol	Aromatic addition polymer which is photoconducting.
potential energy diagrams	Show changes in energy which occur during a reaction.
primary alcohol	Alcohol with — OH group on end carbon atom.
protein	Natural polymer formed by condensation of amino acids.
proton	Positive sub-atomic particle.
radioisotopes	An isotope which is unstable and radioactive.
raw materials	Sources of feedstocks for the chemical industry.
redox reaction	Reaction involving the loss and gain of electrons.
reducing agent	Substance which gives electrons to an atom or ion and is oxidised itself.
reduction	The gain of electrons by an atom or ion.

reduction (organic)	The loss of oxygen or the gain of hydrogen by a molecule.
refining (oil)	Processes which separate and alter the constituents of crude oil.
reforming	Series of reactions which change the structure but not necessarily the size of hydrocarbon molecules.
renewable source	Resource which is not used up or can be reformed within a reasonable length of time.
reversible reaction	Reaction in which products can reform reactants.
salt	Compound formed by an acid and base, replacing the H^+ ions of the acid by another positive ion.
saturated hydrocarbon	Hydrocarbon which contains only C — C single bonds.
screening effect	Inner electron shells shielding the outer electrons from the attraction of the nuclear charge.
secondary alcohol	Alcohol with — OH group on middle carbon atom.
soap	Salt of fatty acid, formed by the alkaline hydrolysis of a fat or oil.
spectator ion	Ion which remains unchanged during a chemical reaction.
standard enthalpy change	Enthalpy change caused by a reaction involving one mole of a substance under standard conditions.
strong acid	Acid which breaks up completely into ions.
strong alkali	Alkali which breaks up completely into ions.
sub-atomic particle	Particles which make up the atom's structure.
surface catalyst	Catalyst which acts by adsorbing reactant molecules onto its surface.
synthesis gas	Mixture of carbon monoxide and hydrogen formed by steam reforming of coal or methane.
temperature	Measure of the average kinetic energy of the molecules of a substance.
tertiary alcohol	Alcohol with — OH group on carbon atom attached to three other carbons.
thermal cracking	Breaking up long chain hydrocarbons by the action of heat alone.
thermosetting polymer	Polymer with cross-links which sets hard when formed and will not melt on heating.
thermosoftening polymer	Polymer with independent chains which softens or melts on heating.
titration	A technique used to find the exact volumes of two solutions which are needed for complete reaction.
triglyceride	A fat or oil molecule with three acid molecules combined with one glycerol molecule.
unleaded petrol	Petrol which has a high proportion of branched and aromatic molecules added to raise octane rating.
unsaturated hydrocarbon	Hydrocarbon which contains at least one C $=$ C double bond or C $\equiv$ C triple bond.
Van der Waals' forces	Weak forces of attraction between all atoms and molecules caused by uneven electron distribution.
variable costs	Manufacturing costs which increase with increased production.
viscosity	Thickness of a liquid and how easily it pours.
weak acid	Acid which does not completely form ions in solution but retains some molecules.
weak alkali	Alkali which does not completely form ions in solution but retains some molecules.

ELECTRON ARRANGEMENTS OF ELEMENTS

Key

| Atomic Number |
| Symbol |
| Electron arrangement |
| Name |

| 1 | H | 1 | Hydrogen |

Main Groups

Group 1	Group 2	Group 3	Group 4	Group 5	Group 6	Group 7	Group 0
							2 **He** 2 Helium
1 **Li** 2,1 Lithium	4 **Be** 2,2 Beryllium	5 **B** 2,3 Boron	6 **C** 2,4 Carbon	7 **N** 2,5 Nitrogen	8 **O** 2,6 Oxygen	9 **F** 2,7 Fluorine	10 **Ne** 2,8 Neon
11 **Na** 2,8,1 Sodium	12 **Mg** 2,8,2 Magnesium	13 **Al** 2,8,3 Aluminium	14 **Si** 2,8,4 Silicon	15 **P** 2,8,5 Phosphorus	16 **S** 2,8,6 Sulphur	17 **Cl** 2,8,7 Chlorine	18 **Ar** 2,8,8 Argon
19 **K** 2,8,8,1 Potassium	20 **Ca** 2,8,8,2 Calcium	31 **Ga** 2,8,18,3 Gallium	32 **Ge** 2,8,18,4 Germanium	33 **As** 2,8,18,5 Arsenic	34 **Se** 2,8,18,6 Selenium	35 **Br** 2,8,18,7 Bromine	36 **Kr** 2,8,18,8 Krypton
37 **Rb** 2,8,18,8,1 Rubidium	38 **Sr** 2,8,18,8,2 Strontium	49 **In** 2,8,18,18,3 Indium	50 **Sn** 2,8,18,18,4 Tin	51 **Sb** 2,8,18,18,5 Antimony	52 **Te** 2,8,18,18,6 Tellurium	53 **I** 2,8,18,18,7 Iodine	54 **Xe** 2,8,18,18,8 Xenon
55 **Cs** 2,8,18,18,8,1 Caesium	56 **Ba** 2,8,18,18,8,2 Barium	81 **Tl** 2,8,18,32,18,3 Thallium	82 **Pb** 2,8,18,32,18,4 Lead	83 **Bi** 2,8,18,32,18,5 Bismuth	84 **Po** 2,8,18,32,18,6 Polonium	85 **At** 2,8,18,32,18,7 Astatine	86 **Rn** 2,8,18,32,18,8 Radon
87 **Fr** 2,8,18,32,18,8,1 Francium	88 **Ra** 2,8,18,32,18,8,2 Radium						

TRANSITION ELEMENTS

21 **Sc** 2,8,9,2 Scandium	22 **Ti** 2,8,10,2 Titanium	23 **V** 2,8,11,2 Vanadium	24 **Cr** 2,8,13,1 Chromium	25 **Mn** 2,8,13,2 Manganese	26 **Fe** 2,8,14,2 Iron	27 **Co** 2,8,15,2 Cobalt	28 **Ni** 2,8,16,2 Nickel	29 **Cu** 2,8,18,1 Copper	30 **Zn** 2,8,18,2 Zinc
39 **Y** 2,8,18,9,2 Yttrium	40 **Zr** 2,8,18,10,2 Zirconium	41 **Nb** 2,8,18,12,1 Niobium	42 **Mo** 2,8,18,13,1 Molybdenum	43 **Tc** 2,8,18,13,2 Technetium	44 **Ru** 2,8,18,15,1 Ruthenium	45 **Rh** 2,8,18,16,1 Rhodium	46 **Pd** 2,8,18,18,0 Palladium	47 **Ag** 2,8,18,18,1 Silver	48 **Cd** 2,8,18,18,2 Cadmium
57 **La** 2,8,18,18,9,2 Lanthanum	72 **Hf** 2,8,18,32,10,2 Hafnium	73 **Ta** 2,8,18,32,11,2 Tantalum	74 **W** 2,8,18,32,12,2 Tungsten	75 **Re** 2,8,18,32,13,2 Rhenium	76 **Os** 2,8,18,32,14,2 Osmium	77 **Ir** 2,8,18,32,15,2 Iridium	78 **Pt** 2,8,18,32,17,1 Platinum	79 **Au** 2,8,18,32,18,1 Gold	80 **Hg** 2,8,18,32,18,2 Mercury
89 **Ac** 2,8,18,32,18,9,2 Actinium									

LANTHANIDES

57 **La** 2,8,18,18,9,2 Lanthanum	58 **Ce** 2,8,18,20,8,2 Cerium	59 **Pr** 2,8,18,21,8,2 Praseodymium	60 **Nd** 2,8,18,22,8,2 Neodymium	61 **Pm** 2,8,18,23,8,2 Promethium	62 **Sm** 2,8,18,24,8,2 Samarium	63 **Eu** 2,8,18,25,8,2 Europium	64 **Gd** 2,8,18,25,9,2 Gadolinium	65 **Tb** 2,8,18,27,8,2 Terbium	66 **Dy** 2,8,18,28,8,2 Dysprosium	67 **Ho** 2,8,18,29,8,2 Holmium	68 **Er** 2,8,18,30,8,2 Erbium	69 **Tm** 2,8,18,31,8,2 Thulium	70 **Yb** 2,8,18,32,8,2 Ytterbium	71 **Lu** 2,8,18,32,9,2 Lutetium

ACTINIDES

89 **Ac** 2,8,18,32,18,9,2 Actinium	90 **Th** 2,8,18,32,18,10,2 Thorium	91 **Pa** 2,8,18,32,20,9,2 Protactinium	92 **U** 2,8,18,32,21,9,2 Uranium	93 **Np** 2,8,18,32,22,9,2 Neptunium	94 **Pu** 2,8,18,32,24,8,2 Plutonium	95 **Am** 2,8,18,32,25,8,2 Americium	96 **Cm** 2,8,18,32,25,9,2 Curium	97 **Bk** 2,8,18,32,27,8,2 Berkelium	98 **Cf** 2,8,18,32,28,8,2 Californium	99 **Es** 2,8,18,32,29,8,2 Einsteinium	100 **Fm** 2,8,18,32,30,8,2 Fermium	101 **Md** 2,8,18,32,31,8,2 Mendelevium	102 **No** 2,8,18,32,32,8,2 Nobelium	103 **Lr** 2,8,18,32,32,9,2 Lawrencium

RELATIVE ATOMIC MASSES OF SELECTED ELEMENTS
(simplified for calculations)

Element	Symbol	Relative atomic mass	Element	Symbol	Relative atomic mass
aluminium	Al	27	magnesium	Mg	24
argon	Ar	40	mercury	Hg	201
bromine	Br	80	neon	Ne	20
calcium	Ca	40	nickel	Ni	59
carbon	C	12	nitrogen	N	14
chlorine	Cl	35·5	oxygen	O	16
copper	Cu	64	phosphorus	P	31
fluorine	F	19	platinum	Pt	195
gold	Au	197	potassium	K	39
helium	He	4	silicon	Si	28
hydrogen	H	1	silver	Ag	108
iodine	I	127	sodium	Na	23
iron	Fe	56	sulphur	S	32
lead	Pb	207	tin	Sn	119
lithium	Li	7	zinc	Zn	65

FORMULAE OF SELECTED IONS CONTAINING MORE THAN ONE KIND OF ATOM

one positive		one negative		two negative		three negative	
Ion	Formula	Ion	Formula	Ion	Formula	Ion	Formula
ammonium	NH_4^+	ethanoate	CH_3COO^-	carbonate	CO_3^{2-}	phosphate	PO_4^{3-}
		hydrogencarbonate	HCO_3^-	chromate	CrO_4^{2-}		
		hydrogensulphate	HSO_4^-	dichromate	$Cr_2O_7^{2-}$		
		hydrogensulphite	HSO_3^-	sulphate	SO_4^{2-}		
		hydroxide	OH^-	sulphite	SO_3^{2-}		
		nitrate	NO_3^-				
		permanganate	MnO_4^-				

ELECTROCHEMICAL SERIES:
STANDARD REDUCTION POTENTIALS

Reaction		E°/V
Li^+ (aq) + e^-	$\rightleftharpoons$ Li (s)	−3·02
Cs^+ (aq) + e^-	$\rightleftharpoons$ Cs (s)	−2·92
Rb^+ (aq) + e^-	$\rightleftharpoons$ Rb (s)	−2·92
K^+ (aq) + e^-	$\rightleftharpoons$ K (s)	−2·92
Sr^{2+} (aq) + $2e^-$	$\rightleftharpoons$ Sr (s)	−2·89
Ca^{2+} (aq) + $2e^-$	$\rightleftharpoons$ Ca (s)	−2·76
Na^+ (aq) + e^-	$\rightleftharpoons$ Na (s)	−2·71
Mg^{2+} (aq) + $2e^-$	$\rightleftharpoons$ Mg (s)	−2·37
Al^{3+} (aq) + $3e^-$	$\rightleftharpoons$ Al (s)	−1·70
Zn^{2+} (aq) + $2e^-$	$\rightleftharpoons$ Zn (s)	−0·76
Cr^{3+} (aq) + $3e^-$	$\rightleftharpoons$ Cr (s)	−0·74
Fe^{2+} (aq) + $2e^-$	$\rightleftharpoons$ Fe (s)	−0·41
Ni^{2+} (aq) + $2e^-$	$\rightleftharpoons$ Ni (s)	−0·23
Sn^{2+} (aq) + $2e^-$	$\rightleftharpoons$ Sn (s)	−0·14
Pb^{2+} (aq) + $2e^-$	$\rightleftharpoons$ Pb (s)	−0·13
Fe^{3+} (aq) + $3e^-$	$\rightleftharpoons$ Fe (s)	−0·04
$2H^+$ (aq) + $2e^-$	$\rightleftharpoons$ H_2 (g)	0·00
Sn^{4+} (aq) + $2e^-$	$\rightleftharpoons$ Sn^{2+} (aq)	0·15
Cu^{2+} (aq) + e^-	$\rightleftharpoons$ Cu^+ (aq)	0·16
SO_4^{2-} (aq) + $2H^+$ (aq) + $2e^-$	$\rightleftharpoons$ SO_3^{2-} (aq) + H_2O (l)	0·20
Cu^{2+} (aq) + $2e^-$	$\rightleftharpoons$ Cu (s)	0·34
I_2 (s) + $2e^-$	$\rightleftharpoons$ $2I^-$ (aq)	0·54
Fe^{3+} (aq) + e^-	$\rightleftharpoons$ Fe^{2+} (aq)	0·77
Ag^+ (aq) + e^-	$\rightleftharpoons$ Ag (s)	0·80
Hg^{2+} (aq) + $2e^-$	$\rightleftharpoons$ Hg (l)	0·85
Br_2 (l) + $2e^-$	$\rightleftharpoons$ $2Br^-$ (aq)	1·07
O_2 (g) + $4H^+$ (aq) + $4e^-$	$\rightleftharpoons$ H_2O (l)	1·23
$Cr_2O_7^{2-}$ (aq) + $14H^+$ (aq) + $6e^-$	$\rightleftharpoons$ $2Cr^{3+}$ (aq) + $7H_2O$ (l)	1·33
Cl_2 (aq) + $2e^-$	$\rightleftharpoons$ $2Cl^-$ (aq)	1·36
MnO_4^- (aq) + H^+ (aq) + $5e^-$	$\rightleftharpoons$ Mn^{2+} (aq) + $4H_2O$ (l)	1·49
F_2 (g) + $2e^-$	$\rightleftharpoons$ $2F^-$ (aq)	2·85

Note The data given above are reduction potentials applicable to standard state conditions.

SI UNITS

QUANTITY	NAME OF UNIT	SYMBOL
length	metre	m
mass	kilogramme	kg
time	second	s
electric current	ampere	A
temperature	kelvin	K
energy	joule	J
electric charge	coulomb	C
electric potential difference	volt	V

PHYSICAL CONSTANTS

QUANTITY	SYMBOL	VALUE
charge on electron	e	$1 \cdot 6 \times 10^{-19}$ coulombs
Avogadro constant	L	$6 \cdot 02 \times 10^{23}$ mol^{-1}
Faraday	F	$9 \cdot 65 \times 10^4$ coulombs mol^{-1}
Planck constant	h	$6 \cdot 63 \times 10^{-34}$ J s
speed of light in vacuum	c	$3 \cdot 00 \times 10^8$ m s^{-1}

SI PREFIXES AND MULTIPLICATION FACTORS

SI PREFIX	SYMBOL	MULTIPLICATION		
tera	T	1 000 000 000 000	=	10^{12}
giga	G	1 000 000 000	=	10^9
mega	M	1 000 000	=	10^6
kilo	k	1 000	=	10^3
deci	d	$\cdot$1	=	10^{-1}
centi	c	$\cdot$01	=	10^{-2}
milli	m	$\cdot$001	=	10^{-3}
micro	μ	$\cdot$000 001	=	10^{-6}
nano	n	$\cdot$000 000 001	=	10^{-9}
pico	p	$\cdot$000 000 000 001	=	10^{-12}

CONVERSION FACTORS

For Volume

1 litre	=	1 dm^3	=	1000 cm^3
1000 litres	=	1000 dm^3	=	1 m^3

For Temperature

0 °C = 273 K

ENTHALPIES OF FORMATION AND COMBUSTION OF SELECTED SUBSTANCES

Substance	Standard enthalpy of formation /kJ mol⁻¹	Standard enthalpy of combustion /kJ mol⁻¹
hydrogen	—	− 286
carbon (graphite)	—	− 394
sulphur (rhombic)	—	− 297
methane	− 75	− 882
ethane	− 85	−1542
propane	−104	−2202
butane	−125	−2877
benzene	49	−3273
ethene	52	−1387
ethyne	227	−1305
methanol	−239	− 715
ethanol	−278	−1371
propan-1-ol	—	−2010
methanoic acid	−409	− 263
ethanoic acid	−487	− 876

IONISATION ENERGIES AND ELECTRONEGATIVITIES OF SELECTED ELEMENTS

Element	Symbol	Ionisation Energies / kJ mol−1				Electro-negativity (Pauling scale)
		First	Second	Third	Fourth	
hydrogen	H	1320	—	—	—	2·1
helium	He	2380	5260	—	—	—
lithium	Li	526	7310	11800	—	1·0
beryllium	Be	905	1770	14800	—	1·5
boron	B	807	2440	3660	25000	2·0
carbon	C	1090	2360	4640	6220	2·5
nitrogen	N	1410	2860	4580	7470	3·0
oxygen	O	1320	3400	5320	7470	3·5
fluorine	F	1690	3380	6140	8410	4·0
neon	Ne	2090	3960	6140	9360	—
sodium	Na	502	4560	6920	9540	0·9
magnesium	Mg	744	1460	7750	10500	1·2
aluminium	Al	584	1830	2760	11600	1·5
silicon	Si	792	1590	3250	4350	1·8
phosphorus	P	1020	1920	2930	4950	2·1
sulphur	S	1010	2260	3380	4560	2·5
chlorine	Cl	1260	2310	3840	5160	3·0
argon	Ar	1530	2670	3950	5770	—
potassium	K	425	3060	4440	5880	0·8
calcium	Ca	596	1160	4930	6470	1·0
scandium	Sc	637	1250	2410	7130	1·3
titanium	Ti	664	1320	2670	4170	1·5
vanadium	V	656	1430	2850	4600	1·6
chromium	Cr	659	1600	3000	4800	1·6
manganese	Mn	723	1520	3270	5000	1·5
iron	Fe	766	1570	2970	5480	1·8
cobalt	Co	764	1660	3250	—	1·8
nickel	Ni	743	1770	3410	5400	1·8
copper	Cu	751	1970	3570	5700	1·9
zinc	Zn	913	1740	3850	5990	1·6
arsenic	As	953	1800	2750	4830	2·0
bromine	Br	1150	2100	3480	4560	2·8
rubidium	Rb	409	2670	3880	—	0·8
strontium	Sr	556	1080	4120	5500	1·0
silver	Ag	737	2080	3380	—	1·9
tin	Sn	715	1420	2960	3930	1·8
antimony	Sb	816	1610	2460	4260	1·9
iodine	I	1020	1850	2040	—	2·5
caesium	Cs	382	2440	—	—	0·7
barium	Ba	509	979	3420	—	0·9
gold	Au	896	1990	—	—	2·4
lead	Pb	722	1460	3100	4080	1·8

Notes: The first ionisation energy for an element E refers to the reaction $E\,(g) \rightarrow E^+\,(g) + e^-$; the second ionisation energy refers to $E^+\,(g) \rightarrow E^{2+}\,(g) + e^-$; etc.

Printed by Bell & Bain Ltd., Glasgow, Scotland.